Architects of Information Advantage
The MITRE Corporation since 1958

Davis Dyer
Michael Aaron Dennis

The Library of Congress has catalogued this edition as follows:
Dyer, Davis.
Architects of information advantage: the MITRE Corporation since
1958 / by Davis Dyer, Michael Aaron Dennis.
p. cm.
Includes bibliographical references and index.
ISBN 1-58192-012-1
1. MITRE Corporation—Case studies. 2. United States—Defense—
Data processing. 3. Information technology—United States.
4. Command and control systems United States. 5. Administrative
agencies—United States—Data processing. I. Dennis, Michael
Aaron, 1960– . II. Title.
U394.B42D95 1998
355.3'43—dc21   98-50027
                                         CIP

Published by Community Communications,
Montgomery, Alabama

First Edition published 1998.
Printed in the United States of America.

Contents

Preface

It is now some forty years since an agreement between President Eisenhower and MIT's President James Killian (then on leave to serve as the President's science advisor) led to the founding of The MITRE Corporation. In 1958, no one could have foretold the astonishing implications that the newly emerging technologies that engaged MITRE would ultimately have for U.S. military capabilities, for U.S. military strategy, and, indeed, for the nation as a whole. Even two decades ago, when *MITRE: The First Twenty Years* was written, could anyone have foreseen the continuing explosion of technology and the resulting transformation of the military establishment? Indeed, the story of MITRE is a tale of the stunning and growing impact of information technology on the way the nation handles and thinks about its security problems.

The eminent Prussian strategist, Karl von Clausewitz, laid great stress on the command difficulties posed by what he called the "fog of war." Insightful as he was, Clausewitz remained in several senses earth-bound. By contrast, today we have the availability of spacecraft, modern sensors, and advanced communications. To an extent that Clausewitz could not have imagined, these have permitted us to dispel the "fog of war"—and thereby to alter the nature of military strategy. Today, Dominant Battlefield Awareness provides an immense military advantage for the United States and its allies. It is an advantage that we must strive to retain.

That advantage was displayed to the entire world in the massive and generally painless victory of the Coalition in the Gulf War. One could even sympathize with Saddam's unfortunate generals. While they were thrust deeply into the "fog of war" by the devastating attack on their sensors and communications, their American counterparts possessed almost total battlefield situation awareness. Put together with precision weapons, that victory was built on information technology and the tying together of various systems.

When MITRE was created in 1958, no one could have anticipated the sophisticated and integrated systems of command, control, communications, and intelligence on display in the Gulf War. The company's first task was the linking of radars, computers, and communications in the SAGE system for vectoring interceptor aircraft to defend America's airspace. To be sure, air defense later lost

v

much of its relevance, as the offensive strategy of the Soviet Union shifted towards ballistic missile attack. Yet SAGE constituted an early, though relatively rudimentary, "system of systems." Over the years, MITRE has moved steadily away from supporting command and control features of single-weapon systems for the Air Force toward the integration of more and more complex systems of systems for sponsors across the Defense Department. Perforce, the company has increasingly focused on information management and on the accelerating revolution in information technology. MITRE has been a substantial contributor to, and part of, the revolution in military tactics and strategy—an almost serendipitous development. Yet the company's contributions are part of a continuing trip to an unknown destination that includes risks that cannot be calculated.

While we seek to exploit the advantages given us through information technology, we must also be aware of our vulnerabilities. Like the inspired inventor of rugby football, we are too inclined to believe that we alone can pick up the ball and run with it. Nonetheless, our high dependency on information technology means that the United States may be more vulnerable to Information Warfare than any other nation. Such vulnerability is not, regrettably, limited to the Department of Defense, which has confronted the problem in military exercises such as Fort Franklin (in which MITRE played a key role) and Eligible Receiver and is working on countermeasures. No doubt, Information Warfare will itself become dominated by countermeasures and counter-countermeasures. The Department is energetically pursuing what it calls Information Assurance. The word, assurance, may itself be seductively reassuring—and full assurance is, no doubt, an unachievable goal. Nonetheless, if we are serious about the problem and work industriously at it, there is little question that in military matters we can remain far ahead of any potential attacker.

To be sure, conditions today are dramatically different from those in the past. Although in the past the military services were at the forefront of technology development, the private sector today sets the pace, a circumstance that means sophisticated equipment and components are widely available commercially. Also, the globalization of the economy means that now such equipment is readily available to others, while in the past access could be restricted—and thereby somewhat delayed. On this question, many in this country are behind the times. It remains a deeply ingrained belief that we can withhold technology from our adversaries. Many believe that restrictions on U.S. sales of such items as supercomputers can accomplish more than is really possible. This belief is illustrated by the recent debate whether the sale of a supercomputer to India was instrumental in that country's development of nuclear weapons. Widespread commercial development of advanced technologies and their global spread has reduced America's ability to deny such technologies to others.

Yet, our greatest vulnerability may lie outside of the military realm. The President's Commission on Critical Infrastructure Protection reported last year on the vulnerabilities of such critical sectors of our economy as finance, electric power, transportation, and communications. Shoring up these sectors against possible attack is an integral part of assuring the nation's security. We must always bear in mind that national security is far broader than military operations or the military establishment. We must attend to such private-sector vulnerabilities. We would have to do so under any circumstances, especially because of the special role that the United States has assumed in international affairs.

Such reflections lead us to another crucial area of MITRE activity—the ongoing research and development activity for the Federal Aviation Administration conducted through a separate FFRDC. Yet, in matters of substance, there is considerable overlap between MITRE's two main areas of activity. Though this may strike outsiders as somewhat anomalous, one must remember the origins of MITRE and the development of SAGE. The techniques of air traffic control and air defense overlap to such an extent that they are virtually congruent. In this light, MITRE's activities in support of the FAA represent a natural development. The overlap, quite naturally, continues down to the present day, and in some respects may be expanding. Air traffic control—on a worldwide basis—is becoming increasingly dependent upon the Global Positioning System, a technology developed by the U.S. Air Force. Harmonization in the use and the expansion of the Global Positioning System has been sought through coordinated planning between the Departments of Defense and Transportation in the Interagency GPS Executive Board.

Over the years, the challenge of air traffic control has steadily grown with the explosion of air travel, and the congestion of airports and air corridors, compounded by weather. Through the Global Positioning System, the challenge of air traffic management will be eased, particularly for transoceanic travel and weather-compounded airport congestion. We may even look forward to the day of "free flight" when aircraft need no longer be vectored along predetermined air corridors. Since air travel is international, of necessity there must be close coordination with the aviation authorities in other countries. We shall need to move toward global standards, most notably for the Global Positioning System itself. Moreover, since there is but one airspace, in all nations there will need to be close collaboration between the civilian and military authorities.

What of the future of the U.S. military? Here, too, we can see a continuing trend towards greater integration and better coordination through information technology. A clear lesson of the Gulf War, accepted by all parties, is the need for jointness. Clearly, this is the case for the military services, so that jointly they can better share information and coordinate their operations. But it is also clear that jointness is desired with allies in coalition warfare.

The Gulf War underscored another aspect of coordination. It was less a lesson than a demonstration of the immense benefits of tying together organizational units, sensors, delivery systems, and weapons in a devastating attack. In this book, you will read of the developments of AWACS and Joint STARS and how they were so effectively tied together with attack systems in the Gulf War. You will also read about the developments of JTIDS, which now helps provide a common intelligence picture to all tactical units. As a former Director of Central Intelligence, I am both impressed and astonished by the value of information systems such as the MITRE-developed Intelink, also covered in this book, which integrates intelligence information across the various agencies constituting the U.S. intelligence community. This illustrates how MITRE's role has increasingly involved working across organizational boundaries and engineering *systems of systems of systems*. What we see ever more clearly is a new vision of how to conduct military operations.

As I indicated at the outset, at the time of MITRE's founding in 1958, no one could have foreseen the increasingly complex and critical role the company would come to play in the transformation of military capabilities and strategy. In recent years, both the emphasis on effective conduct of joint or even coalition operations and Information Warfare (either exploiting advantages or diminishing vulner-abilities) have emerged as preeminent issues for our military establishment. MITRE's expertise in information systems and applications across the DOD and in Information Warfare has raised its service to the government to an unanticipated level of prominence. MITRE's role in helping to transform first the command and control capabilities of the Air Force, and then those of the other military services, has been dramatic.

The MITRE Corporation was established to serve the public interest—and continues to serve the public interest. For more than a decade, I have had the privilege of providing guidance for MITRE. I have been impressed continually by the high quality, professionalism, and dedication of MITRE employees. I am proud of my association with an organization that contributes so much to our nation's technological preeminence. If somehow President Eisenhower, who understood the "fog of war," could see today the results of MITRE's work, I'm sure that he would be astonished and pleased by the immense improvement in military capability that the company has helped to bring about.

August 1998
James Schlesinger
Chairman, Board of Trustees
The MITRE Corporation

The military systems that facilitated the decisive Coalition victory in the 1991 Gulf War included (l. to r.) the brand-new Joint Surveillance Target Attack Radar System (Joint STARS), the Airborne Warning and Control System (AWACS), and the Patriot antimissile defense system. MITRE served as systems engineer on Joint STARS and AWACS, and helped integrate Patriot into other command and control systems. On their way home, these assets reunited briefly on the flight ramp at Hanscom Air Force Base.

Introduction:
The Information Advantage

Even with the growing distance of time, the rapid progression and lop-sided outcome of the 1990-1991 war in the Persian Gulf continue to astonish. The scale of operations in the conflict, and the fast and efficient manner in which they were conducted, are partly captured by recalling the timeline. It all unfolded in just seven months.

On August 2, 1990, Iraqi troops invaded Kuwait, eventually occupying the country with 500,000 troops. By the end of the year, an international coalition led by the United States and representing more than two dozen nations countered with Operation Desert Shield and sent 800,000 combatants into the Gulf region. On January 16, 1991 (local Baghdad time), the Coalition initiated Operation Desert Storm, unleashing a devastating series of air attacks on Iraq. During the first hours of the aerial campaign, most of Iraq's air defenses, aircraft, and command and control systems were knocked out; during the next 1,000 hours, a dazzling variety of precision-guided weapons systematically hammered Iraqi positions and infrastructure throughout the theater. On February 24, the Coalition mounted its ground offensive against enemy positions. Four days later, it was over: The "mother of all battles" predicted by Iraqi leader Saddam Hussein had metamorphosed into "the mother of all retreats," and Kuwait's sovereignty was restored.

The results of the air and ground wars provided a vivid demonstration of the overwhelming superiority of the Coalition. The following exchange ratios between the respective losses of U.S. and Iraqi forces underscore the point:

Assets Lost	Iraq	United States	Exchange Ratio
Tanks	3,700	4	925:1
Armored Vehicles	2,400	3	800:1
Fighters (Air-to-Air)	36	0	36:0
Artillery	2,600	0	2,600:0
Troops	50,000	180	275:1

Explaining Desert Storm

The staggering results of Desert Storm, the decisiveness of the outcome, and the swiftness of the whole affair startled everyone, combatants, observers, military analysts, journalists, and the general public alike. Something remarkable had happened, an event in military history akin to a handful of great battles in which one side, armed with new capabilities, ignited a revolution in military affairs: the longbow against the armored knight, the rifle against the sword, the tank against the foot soldier. To some observers, such parallels did not go far enough. Writing in the pages of *Foreign Affairs* in the fall of 1991, former top Defense Department official (and future Secretary of Defense) William J. Perry could find "virtually no historical precedent" for the result of Desert Storm, which he attributed to "a revolutionary advance in military capability."[1]

1. William J. Perry, "Desert Storm and Deterrence," *Foreign Affairs* (Fall 1991), 66.

2. William J. Perry, Address at MITRE Trustee Meeting, May 1991.

Perry and other analysts of the conflict noted many explanations for the outcome, including superior leadership and organizational skills, better training and equipment, the U.S.S.R.'s decision to withhold formal technical assistance to Iraq, and outright Iraqi blunders. Yet these factors, Perry concluded, could not come close to explaining "the huge disparity" in the exchange ratios. "The only way to explain these large numbers," he pointed out, "is to note that the Coalition forces had an *excellent view of the battlefield and could take quick advantage of that information,* while the Iraqi forces were operating virtually blindfolded." To his fellow trustees of The MITRE Corporation, Perry likened the conflict to a basketball game in which one team featured players with great peripheral vision while those on the other side were blindfolded. One side would run up the score at will, while the opponent would be lucky to score at all; a final tally of 200 to 0—or more—would scarcely be surprising.[2]

The Coalition's "great peripheral vision" and the Iraqi "blindfold" reflected a massive gap in technological capability that widened further after Iraq's communications infrastructure was destroyed early in the war. The Coalition advantage derived especially from a set of command and control systems that integrated sensors, computers, and communications equipment to channel vital intelligence and targeting information to commanders in near-real time. Relying on a diverse mix of military and commercial technologies—computers, software, sensors, satellites, navigation systems, and communications systems— these "systems of systems" helped to overcome a classical problem in military command—what the Prussian military strategist Karl von Clausewitz called "the fog of war." Clausewitz had coined this phrase to describe the centuries-old command challenges caused by erratic and unreliable flows of information during combat, as well as confusion about what this information actually means. In the Gulf War, the fog dissipated for Coalition commanders. Their command and control systems afforded them an unusually rich and detailed picture of military operations. They possessed information about the precise locations of the enemy and their own forces throughout the conflict. This capability proved devastating to the Iraqis and simultaneously helped keep casualties from friendly fire at extraordinarily low levels for a military engagement of such magnitude.

Above all, the command and control systems demonstrated in Desert Storm revealed new dimensions of modern warfare. The first lesson applied to military strategy by reinforcing an old lesson about the vital significance of information dominance. Superior capability in gathering, processing, and distributing information on the battlefield can yield a formidable military advantage. The second lesson concerned the direction and management of joint operations. The same technologies that enabled the Coalition to achieve information dominance also facilitated tight coordination among land, sea, and air forces, and between the forces of one nation and those of its allies. This pattern of joint operations seems likely to characterize military engagements in the post-Cold War world. The third lesson of Desert Storm exposed a new vulnerability. When Iraq lost its modern communications infrastructure, it lost its ability to "see" the battlefield, and it suffered accordingly. Although Coalition information systems were never threatened during the conflict, they might well be in future operations.

In sum, future historians may look back on the Gulf War as the dawn of a new age of "information warfare." As former Secretary of Defense—and chairman of The MITRE Corporation—James Schlesinger put it, the Gulf War provided "a remarkable display of American technological prowess. We stunned Saddam Hussein and his generals, and it surprised almost everybody else. But we will never be able to surprise others again with the technologies we revealed during that war. So we must work hard to retain our relative technical advantage."[3]

Engineering the Information Advantage

The new military capabilities unveiled during the Gulf War constitute a vital national strategic advantage for the United States in the late 1990s, and they will remain so well into the 21st century. In light of their significance, it is essential to understand how these capabilities came about. They are the product of a long and continuing evolution marked by serendipitous advances and significant contributions from many quarters.

This book focuses on one central actor in the story: The MITRE Corporation, a not-for-profit institution founded in 1958 to provide systems engineering and

MITRE Trustee and future U.S. Secretary of Defense William J. Perry (addressing a MITRE gathering in 1991) saw vastly superior command and control systems behind the Collation victory in the Gulf War.

3. "James Schlesinger Says U.S. Risks Defense Decline," *Insight,* May 4, 1998, 23; c.f., Statement of James Schlesinger before the Armed Services Committee, United States Senate, on the Report of the National Defense Panel, January 29, 1998; and *Critical Foundations: Protecting America's Infrastructures.* The Report of the President's Commission on Critical Infrastructure Protection, October 1997, ix, xi, and 17.

integration services to the U.S. Air Force. Operating at the intersection of advanced technology and vital national concerns, the company grew to serve a variety of government customers at the highest levels. In its 40th year, MITRE operated three Federally Funded Research and Development Centers (FFRDCs), one serving the Department of Defense (DOD), another, the Federal Aviation Administration (FAA), and the third, added in the fall of 1998, in support of the U.S. Internal Revenue Service (IRS).

During its early years, MITRE developed expertise in designing, engineering, and integrating systems of systems for the Air Force, as well as a growing list of government sponsors. By the early 1990s, MITRE-engineered systems were integral components of U.S. military capability. During Operations Desert Shield and Desert Storm, for example, the company's work showed up prominently, in helping to prepare deployment plans, gather and distribute intelligence information, identify targets, coordinate air traffic, manage communications, and support military commanders. (*See Interlude 5 for additional details.*) Thereafter, as this book makes clear, the company continued to work with its DOD sponsors to expedite the gathering, processing, distribution, and display of information for decision makers throughout the chain of command. For the FAA, another long-standing sponsor, MITRE helped engineer and guide the evolution of the U.S. air traffic control system—the biggest and most successful continuously operating system of systems ever developed. And for the IRS, MITRE is assisting the modernization of the information systems and operational processes for tax administration.

In 1958, when MITRE was established, few people expected or forecast such developments. The company's first responsibility, systems engineering for the continental air defense system (called SAGE for the "Semi-Automated Ground Environment") was also the first electronic command and control system and one of the earliest systems of systems. SAGE placed a digital computer at the center of a web of sensors and communications equipment to monitor the airspace along the nation's borders in real time and provide continuous status updates to support decision making by military commanders. At first, SAGE supplemented traditional methods of air defense organization, carried out by cadres of military and civilian personnel. Eventually, SAGE and its successors automated the traditional air defense function. Today's citizens, schooled on video games and the works of writers like Tom Clancy, cannot imagine how that duty was performed in an era before computers.

SAGE represented the first fruits of a continuing revolution wrought through the application of information technology to support military decision making.

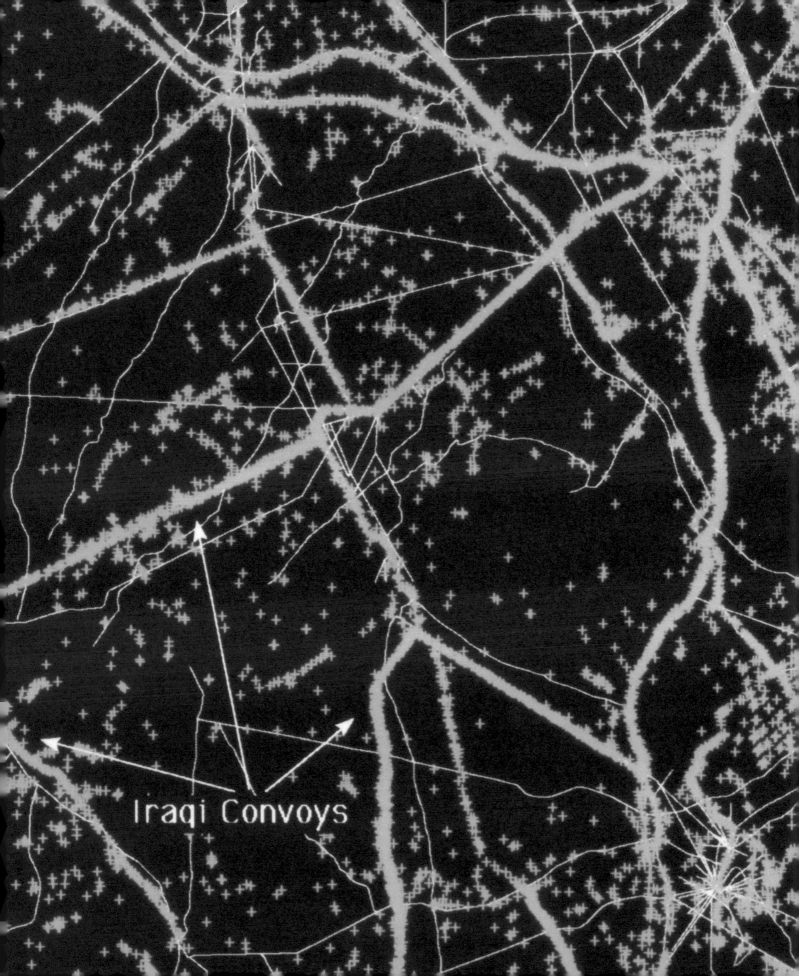

Iraqi Convoys

Today, through the efforts of institutions like MITRE, technology has become the catalyst to continuing and accelerating fundamental change in the way government works. Decision makers have access to an extraordinary volume of information that can be screened and sorted, monitored and updated, and analyzed and interpreted in near-real time, around the clock—all the while engaging a fraction of the personnel once required to deliver much less comprehensive results. Organizational boundaries are being redrawn continuously, and barriers to the flow of information are breaking down everywhere. It matters less and less where on the planet the information originates, where it is processed, or where it is consumed—as the Gulf War amply demonstrated.

MITRE plays a key role in enabling its customers to harness the power of new information technologies and systems. The company's value to the government rests on three characteristics that, as a package, are not available from any other source. First is the high level and quality of MITRE's expertise in information systems (military and commercial) and systems design, engineering, and integration. (In this context, information is taken in the broad sense of the word, encompassing sensor systems like radar and intelligence collection, to the wide range of computers, decision-support software and the entire spectrum of communications systems that are necessary to create end-to-end systems.) Second is what one admiring customer, Victor Ferlise, Deputy to the Commanding General, U.S. Army Communications-Electronics Command, calls "profound knowledge" of the systems and organizations into which new technology must be inserted.[4] MITRE personnel have worked closely with customers in operational environments for many years and often constitute their customers' organizational and technical memory. And third, is the company's position as an operator of FFRDCs, which affords the government impartial advice.

FFRDCs are an unusual type of organization, created in the public interest to occupy the space between government agencies—which may not be able to attract and retain sufficient technical personnel—and industrial contractors subject to profit motives and other underlying imperatives that might be seen as potential conflicts of interest. By agreement with the government and contained within its Articles of Incorporation, MITRE cannot manufacture products, provide services routinely available from industrial contractors, or work for profit seeking organizations. Rather it was created to provide technical capabilities to its sponsors that are not available from any other single source. Its work programs are capped annually, and it cannot compete against industrial contractors for government business.

4. Victor Ferlise interview, December 22, 1997.

Opposite page:

In the Gulf War, the MITRE-engineered Joint STARS provided Coalition commanders with a detailed picture of the movement of enemy ground forces. Pictured opposite: Iraqi convoys flee Kuwait in "the mother of all retreats."

Although these arrangements and restrictions come with obvious costs, such as limits on MITRE's ability to grow, diversify, or even take on new work, they also carry countervailing benefits. The company has expanded its customer base beyond the Air Force because other services and agencies value its technical competence and trust its judgment, while the Air Force has seen that strengthening the company through appropriate work for others is in its own best interest. Similarly, MITRE's role as an independent and objective advisor working in the public interest has helped it in the sensitive task of developing standards and systems that transcend organizational interests and boundaries. As information systems have grown ever more powerful, and as budget pressures have obliged government entities to streamline, economize, and pool their resources, MITRE's role as a facilitator of organization change and interorganizational collaboration has become more prominent. This trend seems likely to extend well into the future.

The Evolution of New Capabilities

The book is organized around six case studies that cumulatively relate the increasingly profound effects of new technology on government capabilities and MITRE's role in facilitating the impact. The cases are linked and framed by narrative interludes that set them in context and carry the story forward in time.

The first case describes the development of SAGE and the circumstances that led to MITRE's birth as an independent, not-for-profit corporation to provide high-level systems engineering services to the Air Force. Making SAGE work required significant advances across a wide array of advanced technologies involving radar, navigation, telecommunications, weapon systems, fundamental computer design, software, graphical displays, and system design and integration. Many of these technologies were not only new, but they were also evolving rapidly. The techniques and capabilities of management developed in such circumstances became a specialized and distinctive expertise that, in turn, became the foundation of The MITRE Corporation and a valuable resource for its customers. At the same time, SAGE clearly demonstrated the power of computers to create significant new military capabilities, especially in warning of potential conflicts.

Following an interlude that describes the redefinition and expansion of MITRE's role in the 1960s in support of the Air Force's new command and control systems and the beginnings of its work for the FAA, the second case concerns the long development of the Airborne Warning and Control System (AWACS). Conceived in the 1960s to support continental air defense along coastal areas, AWACS eventually found much more potent applications as a mobile system for air defense and air traffic management. During Desert Storm, for example, the system provided accurate tracking of Iraqi aircraft and also helped coordinate more than 2,000 Coalition sorties every day. The system has not only been continuously modified and upgraded, but its use has also spread beyond the United States military to allies in Europe, Asia, and the Middle East.

The subsequent interlude deals with the expanding scope of MITRE's services from the late 1960s through the 1970s and beyond, as the company worked on programs not only for military customers but also for civilian government agencies such as NASA and the Departments of Transportation, Energy, and Health and Human Services. Most of this work originated in Washington, and the interlude describes the buildup of the company's Washington Operations.

The next case examines the long, slow development of JTIDS (Joint Tactical Information Distribution System). The program originated in the 1960s around an innovative approach to information distribution on the battlefield conceived and developed by MITRE. It was one of the first attempts to apply digital technology to lift "the fog of war." It was also one of the first attempts to develop an information system to link the military services in tactical combat situations. In this instance, demonstrating the technology proved a small part of the battle, and it required many years of careful development for the system to overcome intra-service rivalries and skepticism to realize its full potential.

The next interlude deals with a key transition in MITRE's role as it became increasingly engaged in developing high-level command and control systems that spanned the DOD. During the 1970s and 1980s it became clear that the capability, complexity, and cost of new information systems transcended the traditional boundaries of projects, programs, and organizations. Rather, these systems crossed—or had potential to cross—many different initiatives and organizations, bringing issues of interconnection, interoperability, and ultimate responsibility to the fore. MITRE's work on the new command and control systems also brought the company into close contact with all branches of the defense establishment, a circumstance that led to many new assignments.

These points are illustrated in the next case, which describes the development of Intelink, a new information system that improves efficiency in integrated communications, interoperability standards, and information exchange across the agencies and services that comprise the U.S. intelligence community. The case highlights several important aspects of MITRE's work, including its ability to adapt commercial information technology quickly for sophisticated government applications and the ability of an FFRDC to bridge the various (and sometimes competing) interests of multiple federal agencies.

The Intelink case is followed by an interlude that focuses on the implications of changing geopolitics—the collapse of the East Bloc—and accelerating development of commercial information technology on government operations. During the late 1980s, government acquisition began a shift away from big program buys toward continuous, evolutionary improvements to existing systems and integration of those systems into bigger systems of systems. For MITRE, these trends entailed growing responsibilities for information technology integration and management across the DOD and other government agencies and necessitated development of new methods of organization and management.

The fifth case explores these themes in the U.S. Army's Force XXI (21st century) initiative. A response both to the expanding capability of new information technology and to new economic and strategic imperatives in the post-Cold War era, Force XXI aims to "digitize the battlefield," bringing together all battlefield information systems and providing a common situational map to all friendly forces in combat from division commanders down to tank company commanders and infantry platoon leaders. When fully operational, this capability will allow every commander, war fighter, unit, vehicle, and weapon system involved in battle to visualize the dynamics of battle and fight as a totally integrated unit. With significant systems engineering support from MITRE, Force XXI technologies performed successfully in several key tests in the mid- and late-1990s.

The last interlude deals with the reexamination of MITRE's operations in the mid-1990s and the company's decision to concentrate on the activities of its DOD and FAA FFRDCs. In 1996, MITRE organized the work performed for other government customers into a wholly separate and unrelated company called Mitretek Systems. The analysis and debates that led to this outcome occurred in a politically charged environment that featured strident criticism of FFRDCs generally. MITRE emerged from this difficult period with a clear sense of its mission and core business and strong support from its customers.

The final case in the book covers the evolution of MITRE's relationship with the FAA, which originated as a natural outgrowth of the company's work on continental air defense. The case focuses on recent initiatives in collaborative air traffic management that promise to bring about a new order of cooperation among public decision makers (air traffic controllers, traffic flow managers, airport authorities, and FAA maintenance staff) and private decision makers (airlines, freight haulers, and general aviation pilots). Collaborative air traffic management will be implemented gradually over many years. One of the first steps is the development of new decision support tools to help air traffic controllers monitor and supervise air traffic in a less structured environment. For example, the MITRE-developed User Request Evaluation Tool (URET) provides controllers with advanced notice of potential conflicts between aircraft in flight. Using information and analysis made possible by URET, controllers can allow aircraft to fly more direct routes while still ensuring air traffic safety. Developed over many years and with extensive participation and involvement of air traffic controllers and other stakeholders, URET is presently undergoing operational evaluation in several FAA facilities.

The concluding chapter of the book is an epilogue that takes stock of MITRE's development, accomplishments, capabilities, and learning. The chapter covers the announcement of the sponsorship of a new MITRE FFRDC by the IRS. Finally, it explores the evolving relationship between the company and its government sponsors—a relationship that both sides characterize as a partnership—and considers the challenges they face together at the dawn of a new century.

Manned Interceptor

NIKE

NORAD Combat Center

Control Center

Long-range Radar

BOMARC

Airborne Long-Range Input

Case One

The SAGE Saga
and the Origins of MITRE

One of the biggest defense programs of the 1950s, the Semi-Automated Ground Environment relied on early digital computers to link sensors and weapon systems for continental air defense. A network of ground-based radar stations supplemented by airborne radar systems along the coasts could identify potential threats at a distance. SAGE then fed this information to aircraft and missile systems to target and coordinate counterattacks.

Although the strategic significance of SAGE diminished as threats to the United States shifted from air to missile attacks, the system spawned significant innovations in sensing, computing, communications, real-time control, and systems engineering. It also gave birth to The MITRE Corporation in 1958.

Pictured on overleaf: The basic components of SAGE included ground- and air-based radar systems, control centers, military command posts, and a variety of weapons to counter an air attack.

The SAGE Saga
and the Origins of MITRE

When The MITRE Corporation was formed in 1958, its founders viewed it as a resource designed for a specific purpose—to provide technical assistance to the U.S. Air Force in an advanced and ambitious program called the Semi-Automated Ground Environment (SAGE).[5] SAGE used digital computers—then a brand-new technology—to monitor the nation's airspace, detect potential threats, and coordinate tactical responses. MITRE's assignment represented an extension of work originally performed by MIT's Lincoln Laboratory but no longer deemed feasible or appropriate for an academic institution to continue as SAGE moved from research and development into an operational phase. As a Federal Contract Research Center chartered in the public interest, MITRE seemed an ideal organizational solution to the military's problem of ensuring high quality and objective technical oversight of the program while avoiding potential conflict-of-interest problems that might emerge if a profit-seeking corporation were to undertake the work.

Yet two aspects of SAGE would have profound and enduring consequences beyond the company's original assignment. First was the dramatic impact of information technology on military capability. The digital computer combined with electronic sensors and advanced communications equipment portended a future in which these technologies would revolutionize the command and control of military operations. Second was the generic nature of SAGE as a "system of systems" that called for specific skills in technology, organization, and management that would prove essential to a host of future military programs. Both aspects—the application of information technology to military purposes, and the design and engineering of systems of systems—resulted in a vital and enduring role for MITRE that transcended the expectations of its founders.

To understand how the continuing development of SAGE made MITRE and MITRE led the evolution of SAGE, it is necessary to follow two separate, yet related series of events: one dealing with the problem of continental air defense, another dealing with the development of the Whirlwind digital computer under the leadership of Jay Forrester in MIT's Servomechanisms Laboratory and Digital Computer Laboratory.

5. For recent surveys of SAGE, see Thomas P. Hughes, *Rescuing Prometheus* (New York: Pantheon Books, 1998), Chapter II; and Paul N. Edwards, *The Closed World: Computers and the Politics of Discourse in Cold War America* (Cambridge, Mass.: The MIT Press, 1996), esp. Chapter 3

The Problem of Continental Defense

For the U.S. Air Force, and its predecessor, the Army Air Force, the best defense was a powerful and overwhelming offense. In July, 1947, President Truman appointed a special Air Policy Commission under the direction of Thomas Finletter, a prominent Philadelphia attorney, to develop a program for both military and civilian aviation. The commission met in the shadow of the 28 July decision to create the Air Force as a separate and independent service, one charged with many responsibilities, including the coordination of the nation's air defense. Finletter's final report, *Survival in the Air Age*, called present and foreseeable Air Force budgets inadequate for the nation's effective defense come "A-Day," 1 January 1953, the earliest possible date when an enemy possessing an atomic bomb might attack the U.S.[6] To counter the A-Day threat, the Finletter Commission proposed that the Air Force's combat groups increase markedly, with a corresponding surge in the number of aircraft on station.[7] For the Finletter Commission and the newly independent Air Force, then, air defense was synonymous with the service's expansion through the acquisition of new aircraft. There was no mention of using radar or other detection technologies to develop a defensive system for the continental United States. Ironically, the report unwittingly made a powerful argument for some type of defensive system other than aircraft through its use of a polar perspective map which showed the routes Soviet bombers and later ballistic missiles would take on their way to American targets. The vast Canadian expanse, as well as the northern United States, stood between the Soviet Union and the destruction of the American heartland.

Although the Air Force had the responsibility for air defense, military aviators were not the only people interested in air defense. Much of the World War II research and development effort had centered on the technologies necessary to detect and destroy attacking aircraft. Chief among these technologies was radar, the use of electromagnetic waves to detect aircraft long before they were visible. MIT's Radiation Laboratory had been one of the major sites for the Allied radar research effort; veterans of the laboratory played important roles in the postwar military research and development system, despite their return to academia and industry. Although the Radiation Laboratory went out of business at the end of 1945, much of the military-oriented research continued in MIT's new Research Laboratory for Electronics (RLE) composed of faculty members from MIT's physics and electrical engineering departments.[8]

Among the novelties of post war research and development was the large role played by universities in the development of new weapons technologies. MIT was certainly a leader in this respect, drawing upon its wartime experiences, but it was

6. On the general history of continental defense, see Kenneth Schaffel, *The Emerging Shield: The Air Force and the Evolution of Continental Air Defense, 1945-1960.* (Washington, DC: Office of Air Force History, 1990). On "A-Day" see Air Policy Commission. (Finletter Commission), *Survival in the Air Age.* (Washington, DC: Government Printing Office, 1948), 19.

7. *Survival in the Air Age*, 25.

8. On the origins of the RLE, see Stuart W. Leslie, *The Cold War and American Science: The Military-Industrial-Academic Complex at MIT and Stanford.* (New York: Columbia University Press, 1993), 25-32.

far from alone. Stanford, Johns Hopkins, Michigan, and the University of California freely assigned scientists and engineers to national defense and security programs and projects. At the same time, academics were not content to leave the nation's defense to the military alone. Working within the services, as well as in new institutions like the Department of Defense's Research and Development Board, the RAND Corporation, and the Air Force's Science Advisory Board, academics initiated or suggested research they believed vital for the U.S. military to preserve national security. It was also research that they believed intellectually interesting and rewarding for their respective institutions. SAGE, the massive continental defense system, was an example of this academic-driven military research.

More specifically, the problem of air defense attracted the interest of George Valley, an MIT physicist and Radiation Laboratory veteran who had served as one of the editors of the multi-volume series of technical works appearing from the laboratory's wartime research and development effort. Those volumes became the cornerstones of much of postwar electrical and electronic engineering. As a member of the Air Force's Science Advisory Board, Valley became interested in the nation's air defense, especially after the Soviets detonated their atomic bomb in 1949. Valley arranged a visit to an Air Force Continental Command radar station, and what he saw appalled him. As he later described it, the site was "one of those army camps of the Indian wars that you see in the late-night movies—except that Quonset huts substituted for log cabins, jeeps took the place of horses, and the officers didn't wear slouch hats."[9] Particularly alarming to Valley was that the radar site communicated with other sites as well as its superiors by high frequency radio. Such radio transmissions were easily affected by the changing character of the ionosphere. When Valley asked why the Air Force did not use the telephone system to move information from the radar site to decision makers, he learned that the Air Force would not allow civilians to handle military communications.

Valley continued his research, visiting the Air Force Cambridge Research Center, which coordinated research of interest to the Service in the greater Boston area. Valley was impressed by the Center's technological developments, particularly the ability to transmit radar images over standard telephone lines. The Center's work was the only bright spot that Valley discovered. Disturbed by his findings, he wrote Air Force Science Advisory Board (SAB) chairman Theodore von Karman in November 1949, suggesting the establishment of a special Board committee to study the air defense problem, using professionals from the fields of physics, electronics, aerodynamics and guided missiles.[10] In December, after the Board

9. George E. Valley, "How the SAGE Development Began." *Annals of the History of Computing* 7, no. 3 (1985), 196-226, 198.

10. Ibid, 199.

11. Ibid, 200.

MIT Professor George Valley addresses the press at the announcement of SAGE early in 1954.

12. Quoted in Kent C. Redmond and Thomas M. Smith. *Project Whirlwind: The History of a Pioneer Computer.* (Bedford, Mass.: Digital Press, 1980), 172–173.

consulted with the Air Force, Valley became chair of the Air Defense System Engineering Committee (ADSEC). Often referred to as the "Valley Committee," the group consisted of seven individuals, six of whom were affiliated with MIT. The group's charge was seemingly simple: "develop equipment and techniques—on an air defense system basis—so as to produce maximum effective air defense for a minimum dollar investment."[11] No one realized what an effective air defense might cost or how long it might take to develop.

Valley's committee met on Fridays at the Air Force Cambridge Research Center. The researchers quickly came to believe that the real problem was one of identifying and tracking low-flying bombers. Existing U.S. radar stations, which consisted of war surplus installations, were effective at detecting high-altitude aircraft, but given their geographically dispersed location, the earth's curvature, and the fact that the attacking Soviet aerial armada would fly low, under the existing radar net, hundreds of continuous-wave radar sets would be necessary. In their final report, ADSEC compared the existing air defense infrastructure "to an animal that was at once 'lame, purblind, and idiot-like'." Of these traits, "idiotic is the strongest. It makes little sense for us to strengthen the muscles if there is no brain; and given a brain, it needs good eyesight."[12] ADSEC's final report envisioned a network of radar stations that would feed their data over telephone lines to central command and control centers. There, the data would be translated onto video screens and different colors would identify friendly and hostile aircraft as well as various interceptor technologies. The key to the display would be a multi-purpose digital computer that could handle the large volume of radar information from the geographically dispersed stations and process that data into a form that was easily represented to military officers who could act on it. It was not coincidental that Valley's final report envisioned a digital computer—one was already under development at MIT.

The system imagined by ADSEC did not exist in 1950. Indeed, its major components, including the new digital computer and novel radar technologies, could be shown to work in principle, but the designs needed continued work. Hence, the ADSEC report suggested that the Air Force establish a laboratory, in the Cambridge area, that would develop the system imagined in the report. To the Air Force, which did not have a large-scale internal R&D organization or arsenal, this seemed an appropriate solution. Research and development allowed for the cementing of relations with MIT, relations that might persist even after the air defense problem was solved. To MIT, however, the plan might prove dangerous; if the Air Force were to suddenly cancel the project, the Institute would be left with the bills, as well as the individuals recruited to work on the system. Before proceeding, Institute administrators, especially President James R. Killian, demanded that another study of air defense take place: Project Charles, under the direction of F. Wheeler Loomis, a University of Illinois physicist and Radiation Lab veteran.

Project Charles was one of the famous "summer studies," an eclectic group of inquiries that one participant, MIT nuclear physicist Jerrold Zacharias, playfully described as "summer studies, some are not."[13] More importantly, summer studies provided an innovative way in which military researchers and academics could work together as equals. Prior to Project Charles, MIT had sponsored two other famous studies—Project Lexington, the nuclear airplane project, and Project Hartwell on anti-submarine warfare. Both studies led to significant research projects at MIT, as well as an influx of government funds. Valley was well aware of the financial benefits MIT might reap from its participation in the air defense effort. Writing to the MIT Academic Council in December 1950, he put forth 11 reasons for forging ahead with the air defense research. None was so pithy or so meaningful as number eight: "Twenty billions are going to be spent anyway on air defense; they may as well be spent wisely."[14]

Under Loomis' leadership, the group met in Cambridge from February through the summer of 1951. Project Charles' final report, Problems of Air Defense, validated the Valley Committee's own study. Loomis and his colleagues called for the establishment of a laboratory to study air defense problems; one that MIT would operate and administer jointly for the Army, the Navy, and the Air Force. According to the report, the new laboratory would be known as Project Lincoln and its work would focus on the development of the ADSEC's centralized system and that "the central coordinating apparatus of this system should be a high speed digital computer."[15] Project Charles legitimated Valley's own plan to have an air defense laboratory, what eventually became the MIT Lincoln Laboratory.

Reaping the Whirlwind

Lincoln Laboratory grew quickly. Within a year there were 550 employees and fast-developing plans for a new facility near Hanscom Field (now Hanscom Air Force Base) in Lexington, Massachusetts. Albert Hill became director when Loomis left to return to Illinois, and George Valley was the laboratory's associate director.[16] The vision of a centrally integrated command and control system for continental air defense required not only new buildings but also new technology, including one of the first working digital computers.

Ironically, the development of a digital computer at MIT was something of a historical accident. During the 1930s, Vannevar Bush, a professor of electrical

13. Quoted in Jack S. Goldstein, *A Different Sort of Time: The Life of Jerrold Zacharias, scientist, engineer, educator* (Cambridge, Mass.: MIT Press, 1992), 98; on summer studies in general see J.R. Marvin and F.J. Weyl. "The Summer Study." *Naval Research Reviews,* August (1966).

14. See 19 December 1950, Valley to Academic Council, RG 341, Entry 10, HQ USAF, Box 8, SAB– Air Defense Systems Engineering, U.S. National Archives, College Park, Maryland.

15. Quote from Eva C. Freeman, ed. *MIT Lincoln Laboratory: Technology in the National Interest.* (Lexington, Mass.: Lincoln Laboratory, 1995), 8.

16. Freeman, *MIT Lincoln Laboratory,* 15.

In the late 1950s, James Killian Jr. took leave from his job as head of MIT to serve as President Eisenhower's Science Advisor. Recognizing the long-term significance of SAGE, he helped to establish MITRE and later served as a trustee.

engineering and later dean of engineering, had made MIT a center of excellence in the design and development of analog computers. Perhaps the most famous of his machines was the "differential analyzer," an elaborate electro-mechanical device that solved differential equations through a complex set of linked cams, gears, and metal rods. The rotation of the various elements literally "drew" a solution to the equations.[17] Among Bush's last students at MIT before he left for Washington and the task of organizing American research and development for World War II was a young Australian, Gordon S. Brown, whose 1938 MIT ScD involved the design of the cinema integraph, a novel analog computational technology. In 1939, Brown took up an appointment as an assistant professor in the department of electrical engineering; within a year he had established the MIT Servomechanisms Laboratory.

The new laboratory performed research on contract for both government and industry. With the war, Brown became deeply involved in the development of automatic control systems for naval fire control equipment—extending the analog paradigm to the battlefield. An important aspect of Brown's laboratory was his desire to give his subordinates, his graduate students and post-doctoral associates, a great deal of freedom in articulating and solving problems. The digital computer was the upshot of this "laissez faire" managerial philosophy.[18]

Among those Brown allowed to follow their own ideas was Jay Forrester, a native Nebraskan who arrived at MIT with an undergraduate electrical engineering degree. He moved to MIT to pursue his graduate work as Brown set up the Servomechanisms Lab; Forrester put his studies on hold as he plunged immediately into the development of new weapons technologies. In 1944, U.S. Navy Captain Luis de Florez approached MIT, his alma mater, about the development of a new flight simulator that would be sufficiently powerful and flexible to simulate aircraft not yet built using analysis and wind tunnel test data. Brown turned the project over to Forrester, one of the laboratory's assistant directors.

By the end of the war, the simulation project had mushroomed in size, complexity, and approach and comprised a major portion of the Servomechanisms Lab.[19] In addition to Forrester, there was Robert R. Everett, an electrical engineering student from Duke University who arrived at Brown's MIT lab in time to meet Forrester and contribute his own frequent displays of technical virtuosity.

As the project grew, it became clear that analog methods were inadequate to the solution of the equations necessary to effectively simulate flight controls. After

17. See Larry Owens, "Vannevar Bush and the Differential Analyzer: The Text and Context of an Early Computer." *Technology and Culture* 27 (1986), 63–95.

18. On Brown and the Servomechanisms Laboratory, see Karl L. Wildes and Nilo A. Lindgren. *A Century of Electrical Engineering and Computer Science at MIT, 1882–1982.* (Cambridge, Mass: MIT Press, 1985), 210–227; and Robert Everett interview, October 24, 1997.

19. On Whirlwind's history, see Redmond and Smith. *Project Whirlwind.* And Karl L. Wildes and Nilo A. Lindgren. *A Century of Electrical Engineering and Computer Science at MIT, 1882–1982.* (Cambridge, Mass.: MIT Press, 1985), 228-237.

Facing page:

Background: The scale of the pioneering Whirlwind digital computer is evident in this scene from the Whirlwind Test Center at MIT. Technician Stephen Dodd (seated) operates the machine, while lab directors Jay Forrester (l.), and Bob Everett look on; in the foreground, technician Ramona Ferenz is seated at the display.

much thought, Forrester began designing a digital machine, which soon acquired the name Project Whirlwind. The ramifications of the change from analog to digital were monumental. The project team was literally pushing the frontiers of technology. Although some digital machines had been designed and built during the war, the most famous of which was the ENIAC machine at the University of Pennsylvania's Moore School of Electrical Engineering, there was no such program at MIT. Forrester, working with reports on ENIAC and other digital computing projects, and with Everett, taught himself how to build a computer. These leaders also drew on contributions from many of MIT's brightest electrical engineering faculty and graduate students.

The machine Forrester began designing was a massive consumer of vacuum tubes, on the order of 10,000 tubes for a working machine. It was difficult to imagine that such devices might work in the machine as the necessary memory—what today we call RAM (random access memory)— but they did. Meanwhile, by 1949 it had become clear that the flight simulator was a dead issue: Whirlwind was a computer project. The digital tail had swallowed the analog dog. Forrester had the staff and students stop working on the cockpit of the simulator that year. Alas, the Navy's Office of Naval Research (ONR) had been paying for a flight simulator, not simply a digital computer. Although the Navy officers responsible for the project believed in Forrester's eventual success, they were concerned about the expense of the project, which was running over $100,000 a month. Even Forrester's promising work on ferrite core memory, what would become essential for all mainframe computers, was insufficient to keep ONR funding at the requisite levels. Fortunately, a chance conversation in a hallway at MIT informed George Valley that the machine needed as the "brain" of his proposed air defense system was being built in the Barta Building on the MIT campus.

Bob Everett (l.) and Jack Jacobs helped to design the Whirlwind computer and directed technical development of SAGE and a host of subsequent MITRE programs and projects.

20. Redmond and Smith, *Project Wirlwind,* 144-178.

When Valley encountered Forrester, Whirlwind was a solution in search of a problem.[20] Through demonstrations and meetings, Forrester and Everett persuaded Valley and others that Whirlwind could process the radar data communicated over telephone lines. By September 1951, the Air Force provided $500,000 and the ONR $280,000 to support the machine's continued development; Whirlwind also left the organizational confines of the Servomechanisms Laboratory and became a separate administrative unit under the direction of Forrester and Everett in the new Digital Computation Laboratory. Within six months the new laboratory had become Division 6 of the newly established Lincoln Laboratory. Whirlwind had a new home, and a new mission.

The Birth of MITRE

The relocation of Division 6 from MIT to Hanscom Field in 1954 proved a key step in the development of the new continental air defense system. Meanwhile, Lincoln had successfully designed and built a scale model, known as the Cape Cod System. This involved integrating the computer with the radar systems and display systems. As Division 6 undertook design of Whirlwind II, a machine that would embody lessons from the first machine, it chose IBM to build the computer that would be used in the SAGE system. For IBM this represented one of the great opportunities in American business history. Access to the Division 6 group gave the IBM engineers access to state-of-the-art computer engineering and programming as well as an advantage over their competition. IBM also saw significant commercial potential in the new technology, an assessment that proved on target, e.g., SABRE, the on-line airline reservation system that IBM later sold, was a direct descendent of the company's work on SAGE.[21]

In 1956 Forrester left Lincoln, returning to MIT as a professor of management. Everett became the head of Division 6 and SAGE's development continued. Increasingly, the problems facing those working on SAGE extended far beyond mundane technical headaches with the computer or the immensity of the programming challenge. Instead, the problem of weapons integration began to appear nearly intractable and out-of-place in a university laboratory. In particular, the task of integrating new guided ground-to-air missiles such as the Air Force's BOMARC and the Army's NIKE posed significant technical and managerial problems.

Integration issues acquired even greater urgency in 1957 with the successful launch of the Soviet Sputnik and worries that the United States had lost its lead in defense technology. Lincoln had designed neither BOMARC nor NIKE; the respective contractors for each weapon, Boeing and Bell, had chosen distinctly different control systems. How were these missile systems and SAGE to be welded together? Technically, it was a massive task, requiring that the SAGE system, and the computer at its core, control weapons speaking a different language. To continue with the linguistic analogy, SAGE would have to translate the BOMARC and NIKE systems languages into the SAGE vocabulary, act upon that material, and then issue orders in a language that the missile systems could understand. Given the independent development styles of the corporations and their respective military sponsors, this was far from simple or obvious. For the Lincoln Laboratory management, as well as the MIT administration, these integration issues represented a long-term challenge that no academic institution should undertake. Attempts at convincing other not-for-profit contractors, such

21. On IBM's development, including the benefits of SAGE, see Emerson Pugh, *Memories That Shaped an Industry: Decisions Leading to IBM System/360* (Cambridge, Mass.: MIT Press, 1984).

as the System Development Corporation, then supporting the SAGE programming effort, to tackle the assignment proved futile. Nor could the Air Force interest either Western Electric or IBM in the work. Although the Air Force recognized the nature of the problem—going so far as to form a SAGE Weapons Integration Group (SWIG) in 1956 and the Air Defense Systems Management Office in summer 1957—nothing could replace the expertise embodied in Lincoln's familiarity with the system that had emerged from the wedding of George Valley's original vision and Forrester's foray into digital computing.

Given the Air Force's inability to find a contractor to take on the task of integrating non-Lincoln weapons and sensors into SAGE, MIT administrators decided to create a new, not-for-profit corporation that would become the Air Force's center of technical advice with respect to SAGE and its future development. The concept of such an entity was not new. The Department of Defense had already sponsored a handful of independent not-for-profit Federal Contract Research Centers, including RAND Corporation, that were neither classified as government laboratories nor affiliated with universities. In this instance, the new corporation was closely tethered to MIT through both contracts and personnel.

MITRE's first group of trustees included (l. to r.) Chairman H. Rowan Gaither, Julius Stratton, Franklin Collbohm, William Webster, and James McCormack, Jr. A retired Air Force general, McCormack gave MITRE its name.

The core of the new company was Lincoln's Division 6; Robert Everett became the company's technical director and his associate John Jacobs, deputy technical director. The corporation's Board of Trustees included: H. Rowan Gaither, chairman of the Board of both the RAND Corporation and the Ford Foundation; Julius Stratton, Acting MIT President and a member of both the RAND and Ford Foundation boards; Franklin Collbohm, a founder and president of RAND as well as trustee of RAND's sibling, the System Development Corporation; William Webster, another RAND and MIT trustee as well as executive vice president of New England Electric System and a former chairman of the Defense Department's

Research and Development Board; and James McCormack, Jr., MIT's vice president of sponsored research, a retired Air Force general, and a founder of the Institute of Defense Analysis, another not-for-profit corporation sponsored by several universities to perform the tasks of the DOD's Weapons System Evaluation Group. McCormack, incidentally, bequeathed the new corporation its name—MITRE—but never explained the choice. Some believed it an acronym for "MIT Research," "MIT Research and Engineering," or "MIT, RAND, and Engineering"; others fixed on the British spelling of a carpentry term meaning to join or fit together, a notion suggesting the company's work in integrating systems. The true significance of the name remains a mystery.[22]

The original MITRE trustees constituted a powerful group, closely tied to the nation's national security establishment and experienced in the new institutions that were necessary to integrate the nation's intellectual resources with the existing military infrastructure. Four of the five were RAND veterans; that is, experienced hands at the Air Force's other major center of technical and strategic advice. Nor was the Ford Foundation connection incidental. Ford had given RAND a crucial working capital loan as that corporation separated from its original parent the Douglas Aircraft Corporation. While Ford would not provide MITRE with such munificence, the Ford connection suggested that MITRE would become a vital asset in the nation's long-term war against the Soviet Union. With trustees like this, the new company's prospects were very bright.[23]

Among the early actions of the Trustees was the selection of MITRE's president, Clair W. "Hap" Halligan, AT&T's Director of Military Engineering, and a veteran of SAGE. Another key corporate officer was Paul Cusick, who managed the company's finances. Additional trustees included Halligan, William T. Golden, the consummate national security insider who investigated the state of American science and technology for Truman during the Korean War; Luis Alvarez, a Radiation Laboratory veteran, and director of the University of California, Berkeley's, Radiation Laboratory; and Lawrence Hafstad, former director of the Johns Hopkins University Applied Physics Laboratory, an Atomic Energy Commission officer, and the vice president of Research for General Motors. These were the men who would guide MITRE during its early and formative years.

Creating MITRE only meant that a new organization existed to handle the daunting task of weapons integration. Bringing BOMARC and NIKE into the SAGE family was a remarkable technical and managerial accomplishment, done with about 500 employees who transferred to MITRE from the Lincoln

AT&T veteran Clair W. "Hap" Halligan served as MITRE's first president between 1958 and 1966.

22. The MITRE Corporation, *MITRE: The First Twenty Years* (Bedford, Mass.: The MITRE Corporation, 1979), 16–18.

23. On the Ford Foundation and the Cold War, see Ford Foundation, "Report of the Study for the Ford Foundation on Policy and Programs" (Detroit: The Ford Foundation, 1949); and William A. Blanpied, ed., *Impacts of the Early Cold War on American Science Policy* (Washington, D.C.: American Association for the Advancement of Science, 1995).

Facing page:

SAGE was originally tested along the northern East Coast in the mid-1950s. Pictured opposite: a SAGE long-range search radar installation on Cape Cod, in South Truro, Massachusetts.

24. Edwards, *The Closed World*, 104-106.

25. Kent C. Redmond and Thomas M. Smith. "From Whirlwind to MITRE: The R&D Story of the SAGE Air Defense Computer." MITRE Archives: unpublished manuscript, 1997. Quote from Epilogue, 3. This text is the most comprehensive discussion of SAGE in existence. It is hoped that it might be published soon.

Laboratory in 1958 and 1959. The first SAGE command center, a concrete, windowless box connected to the outside world of radar stations, air bases, air traffic control centers, and other facilities through telephone lines,[24] became operational on July 1, 1958. Several more came on stream during the following months. Perhaps the nature of the accomplishment was best appreciated by the Air Force. Lieutenant General Arthur C. Agan, the first officer to command a SAGE center compared the task of moving from the previous system to the new computer-based framework as the "equivalent of laying a man out on the table and trying to keep him alive while we used the scalpel and took out his nervous system and put another one in."[25] SAGE was more than an organ transplant, or the technical and political site for the origins of MITRE. It was part of a larger transformation, the beginning of a permanent technical revolution in weapon systems, as the U.S. armed services became ever more dependent upon advanced technology and the engineers who implement it successfully. MITRE was an instrument of and for that revolution.

As for SAGE, 23 Direction Centers became operational by 1963. The system continued to function until 1984 when the last center was closed. Ironically, the threat to which SAGE was the response evaporated just as the system went into service, as the challenge of continental air defense shifted from defeating a massive bomber attack to defending against intercontinental ballistic missiles. SAGE's—and MITRE's—contributions to the development of technology were nonetheless profound. The system spawned a multitude of progeny ranging from advanced surveillance and reconnaissance technologies, to civilian air traffic control systems, to a long stream of military command-and-control systems. Equally important, SAGE demonstrated the value of the emerging discipline of systems engineering and integration that would not only sustain MITRE's growth and development but also propel a continuing revolution in military and government operations.

MITRE TIMELINE

Since its founding forty years ago MITRE has been engaged in numerous programs and projects. Each interlude section in this book highlights some of these in a timeline that also notes major events in world history.

1 The first operating SAGE sector was controlled from a concrete blockhouse at McGuire Air Force Base in New Jersey.

2 MITRE began working for the Federal Aviation Administration, its first and still oldest nondefense customer, shortly after the company formed.

3 MITRE moved from MIT Lincoln Laboratory in

January 31
First U.S. Satellite
"Explorer 1" is launched

January 1
485 employees transfer from
Lincoln Laboratory to MITRE

January 1
Fidel Castro gains control of
Cuba

March 3
Air Force asks MIT to
undertake interim
responsibility for SAGE
systems engineering

March 12
William Webster becomes
chairman of the MITRE
Board of Trustees

April
MITRE purchases Sebastian
Farm in Bedford, Mass.

April 1
Air Force Command and
Control Development
Division is established,
Major General Kenneth P.
Bergquist, commander

May 31
Whirlwind computer shuts
down

June 3
MIT first discusses a nonprofit organization for SAGE
systems engineering

May 1
Soviets shoot American
U-2 plane and capture pilot
Francis Gary Powers

August
1,000th MITRE employee
is hired

June 27
First SAGE sector is
dedicated at McGuire
Air Force Base

August 1
Air Force approves first
direct contract with MITRE

July 21
The MITRE Corporation
is formally incorporated

August 5
Board of Trustees, H. Rowan
Gaither, Chairman, holds
first meeting

August 5
C. W. Halligan becomes first
MITRE president

September 25
E Building on Bedford
property is occupied

September 15
Winter Study group issues
final report

September 1
MITRE signs first contract
with MIT.

September 29
MITRE hosts first symposium,
on track-while-scan systems

September 19
Colorado Springs, Colorado
office opens to support
NORAD development

October 1
R. R. Everett is named first
technical director, J. F. Jacobs
first associate technical
director

October 19
First non-Air Force project,
SATIN (SAGE Air Traffic
Integration), begins

October 1
Congress authorizes
formation of National
Aeronautics and Space
Administration (NASA)

December 15
MITRE hosts Winter Study,
first Air Force-wide
command and control
planning forum

December 31
Federal Aviation Agency
(FAA), created by act of
Congress, commences
operations

1961

1962

1963

1964

Texas Instruments introduces computer featuring integrated circuits

January 20
John F. Kennedy is inaugurated 35th President of the United States

January 16
MITRE is awarded FAA contract for air traffic control study (Project Beacon)

January
MITRE completes first IR&D project (refractometer)

January 15
BMEWS sites are completed

March 20
R. S. Nielsen applies for first MITRE patent

4   5   6   7

April 1
Air Force establishes Electronic Systems Division, Maj. Gen. K. P. Bergquist, commander

April 7
IBM 7090 computer is installed in MITRE computer center

May 1
Charles A. Coolidge becomes chairman of the MITRE Board of Trustees

June 12
MITRE begins work on Ballistic Missile Early Warning System (BMEWS) upgrade project

June 27
MITRE begins work on NORAD Combat Operations Center project

August 13
Berlin Wall is completed

December 15
Last SAGE sector within continental United States is completed

April
IBM 1410 computer becomes operational

May
Tampa, Florida site opens

August 1
NATO work commences, Paris site opens

October
United States forms blockade around Cuba to force withdrawal of Soviet missiles

October 1
DEW line is completed

November
MITRE issues first annual report, gross contract revenues, $29,890,566

May 15
Air Traffic Systems Division establishes Washington office

September
Airborne Long-Range Input (ALRI) system becomes operational

September 4
MITRE obtains contract with Defense Communications Agency (DCA) for technical planning of National Military Command System

September 16
Hardened underground SAGE center at North Bay, Ontario becomes operational

October
Washington Technical Directorate is formed

November 22
President John F. Kennedy is assassinated: Lyndon B. Johnson becomes President

December 3
Systems Design Laboratory at Hanscom Field is dedicated

July 1
Tokyo, Japan site opens

August 7
Congress passes Gulf of Tonkin Resolution, authorizing President Johnson to direct military force in Southeast Asia

January
MITRE begins support to
Advanced Research Projects
Agency

January 21
NASA-Houston site opens

August 1
IR&D program tops $1 million

April 20
NORAD complex at
Cheyenne Mountain is
dedicated

May 1
407L site at Eglin Air Force
Base, Florida is activated

Interlude One

8

From Continental Air Defense
to Command and Control
1958–1966

4   MITRE's first annual report
appeared in 1962

5   The company engineered a
SAGE-like air defense system
in Europe called the NATO
Air Defense Ground
Environment (NADGE)

6   A joint Air Force/MITRE R&D
facility, the System Design
Laboratory, opened in 1963 at
Hanscom Field.

7   From air defense, MITRE
branched into missile defense
with the Ballistic Missile Early
Warning System (BMEWS).

8   The company developed
advanced computing and
communications systems at
the North American Air
Defense Command (NORAD)
Combat Operations Center at
Cheyenne Mountain near
Colorado Springs, Colorado.

From Continental Air Defense to Command and Control, 1958–1966

On the evening of Friday, May 27, 1959, researchers at MIT shut down the Whirlwind computer for a final time. The occasion was marked by a few hours of running old demonstration programs but otherwise there was little celebration. Everyone who had helped develop the machine and investigate its applications had little time to dwell on the past because the future seemed endlessly bright. Whirlwind had ignited a real-time revolution that was moving forward at an accelerating pace.

For MITRE and its government customers, the dawning information age marked a time of optimism and opportunity. One sign of new things to come was the opening in the fall of 1959 of MITRE's new quarters in Bedford, Massachusetts, about five miles from Lincoln Laboratory and Hanscom Field. The "Winter Study," that would lead to the backbone concepts for MITRE's contributions to today's command and control capabilities, was underway. It was to have a profound impact on the development of the company, as noted a bit later. Another sign of change was growing demand for the company's expertise, not only in the U.S. military but also in civilian agencies.

In October 1959, MITRE signed its first contract with a nondefense customer, the Federal Aviation Agency (FAA), an assignment that grew out of earlier research at MIT and Lincoln Lab. The FAA collaborated with the Air Force to engage MITRE on a project called SATIN—SAGE Air Traffic Integration.[26] Directed by David R. Israel (who had written his master's thesis at MIT on the use of computers for air traffic control), SATIN aimed at developing a single, unified system for managing all aircraft in the nation's airspace. The similarity of missions between SATIN and SAGE was obvious—air traffic control is concerned with maintaining separation rather than plotting intercepts—but the underlying technology is the same. As part of the program, MITRE modified a SAGE center at Great Falls, Montana, into a combined operation for air defense and en route civilian air traffic control—twin functions carried out successfully for nearly 15 years.[27]

MITRE's strong performance on SATIN enabled the company to withstand a major shift in government policy during the early 1960s. The new, cost-conscious Kennedy administration abandoned efforts to build a common system for both air defense and air traffic control, instead devising a plan—the National Airspace System (NAS) to automate control of civilian air space alone. (*See Case 6.*) By then, MITRE had

Facing page:

As a technician counted down the final minutes of the Whirlwind computer, the revolution in command and control was just beginning.

26. This program represented a follow on to work carried out at Lincoln Laboratory started in 1958 before MITRE's birth. The program was called the Civil Aeronautics Administration [predecessor to the FAA] High-Altitude Remote Monitor (CHARM) during 1958-1959. See MITRE Corporation, *MITRE: The First Twenty Years* (Bedford, Mass.: The MITRE Corporation, 1979), 27

27. MITRE Corporation, *The MITRE Corporation: Challenge and Response, 1958-1988* (Bedford, Mass.: The MITRE Corporation, 1989), 26.

proven itself indispensable to the FAA, which continued to rely on the company's assistance in acquiring new technology and in planning, designing, and testing the new system. These activities grew steadily over time, and during the summer of 1963, about two dozen MITRE personnel—representing about half of the contingent working on civilian air traffic control—relocated to a new facility near Washington, D.C.[28]

MITRE's work for the FAA also marked the beginning of the company's diversification into nonmilitary areas. The Air Force encouraged this complementary work, because of concern about its ability to support MITRE in the long run. The diversification strategy emerged slowly and later became much more visible and explicit. During the 1960s, however, nondefense work constituted a small fraction of the company's total activity. And defense customers, especially the Air Force, generated abundant opportunities to expand the company's capabilities, revenues, and employment. The most important development of the era was a broadened conception of MITRE's core mission that transcended systems engineering of continental air defense to assist the development of electronic "command and control systems." This redefinition of roles began soon after the company's birth, but its origins stretched back further in time.

28. MITRE had established a small liaison office in Washington late in 1959. This was a one- or two-person shop, however, before the relocation of personnel working on the National Airspace System.

During the 1950s, the Air Force had launched about a dozen electronic systems (called "L-Systems") that bore at least some family resemblance to SAGE. Developed or proposed as discrete programs, these systems performed multiple functions, including early warning, data processing and communications for various Air Force commands, generation and distribution of tactical information, weather observation and forecasting, and intelligence-gathering. By the summer of 1959, many officials at Air Force headquarters were pointing out the need to coordinate development of at least some of these systems, although there was little consensus about how that might be accomplished. Some people argued that the L-Systems were "tools" like weapons systems and should be developed by industrial prime contractors. Others believed that the L-Systems constituted a new species of military program that sought to integrate diverse, advanced, and rapidly changing technologies that were beyond the capabilities of any industrial contractor to manage. Rather, the challenge required new methods of management, including a special role for not-for-profit entities like MITRE. And a few far-sighted individuals saw that the truly remarkable aspect of the L-Systems was not their technology content but their organizational implications. These systems and their successors would eventually force a restructuring of the functions and responsibilities of the defense establishment.

The Air Force debated how best to oversee the L-Systems for many months and was assisted along the way by several high-level study and analysis groups. One of these, a group of about 140 scientists, engineers, and military personnel, directly engaged many personnel from MITRE. Known as the Winter Study Group, it had a mandate to "insure that the parts [of these various systems] added up to a sensible whole, to eliminate unnecessary redundancy, to insure compatibility within and among systems, and to take full advantage of the growth potential indicated by the state of the art and required by on-coming weapon systems and changing force structures."[29] MITRE supported the Winter Study Group in several ways: by contributing leadership to the group—including Jack Jacobs and Charles Zraket—providing staff assistance, and hosting meetings at the company's headquarters in Bedford.

29. U.S. Air Force Command and Control Development System, *The Challenge of Command and Control* (Bedford, Mass.: Laurence G. Hanscom Field, 1961). 2.

30. John F. Jacobs, *The SAGE Air Defense System: A Personal History* (Bedford, Mass.: The MITRE Corporation, 1986), 160.

The Winter Study Group viewed the L-Systems as something distinctly different from weapons systems or as subsystems to weapons systems. As Jacobs later wrote, the electronic systems had certain common attributes. In particular, these systems

…served a variety of weapons and sensors and supported many functions previously carried on by human operators. These systems… tended to centralize the control and provide management support to upper-echelon command and control functions. They were evolutionary, constantly in the process of growing and adapting to the changing force structure. They also accommodated new and old subsystems and thus their management required contact with the upper echelons of the various operating commands and had to adapt to changing command personnel.[30]

The Winter Study Group adopted similar language, characterizing the L-Systems as "command and control systems"—meaning that, like SAGE, they linked sensing devices in networks, used computers to monitor the sensors and process and analyze the data collected, and presented this information and analysis to military commanders to facilitate timely decision making. A key aspect of such systems was their intimate relationship with the organizations they were intended to support. As a historian of MITRE's earliest years put it, command and control systems were concerned primarily with "organizations and their basic functions, and only secondarily about the gadgetry, electronic or other, that they might need in order to perform their functions adequately." Expanding on the point, this author went on to note that

…it is not primarily a set of "black boxes" that a command and control system engineer designs, but an entire organization. Only when the organization's essential functions are thoroughly thought out can there be a rational basis for deciding what kind and degree of automation is desirable; and, since no one service would fight a war all by itself, the logical unit to be analyzed, configured, and in some degree automated was not the Air Force but the whole military establishment. Moreover, planning a command and control system …

Evolution of Command and Control System

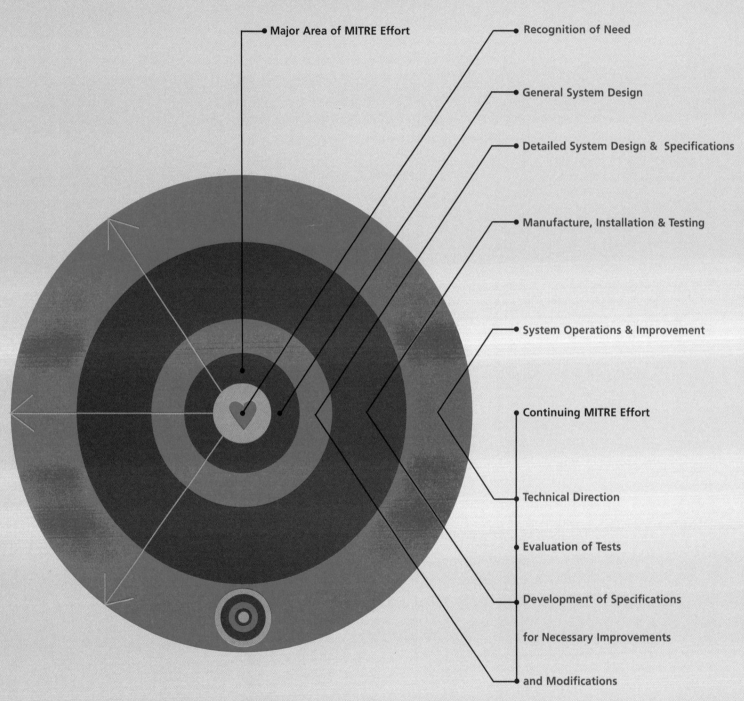

Major Area of MITRE Effort

Recognition of Need

General System Design

Detailed System Design & Specifications

Manufacture, Installation & Testing

System Operations & Improvement

Continuing MITRE Effort

Technical Direction

Evaluation of Tests

Development of Specifications

for Necessary Improvements

and Modifications

is not like planning a building to be built from blueprints; rather, it is a matter of helping the affected organization adopt or evolve a new "life style," a process in which the affected organization must itself participate. [31]

The Winter Study Group's report, issued in September 1960, called for a new, coordinated approach to research and development of Air Force electronic command and control systems, with this responsibility lodged under a single command at Hanscom Field. At the same time, the report urged that future L-Systems be developed in an evolutionary manner to accommodate changes demanded by new threats and technology and that operating military commands should participate actively as designers as well as customers of the systems. Finally, the Winter Study Group also called for "a central system engineering and laboratory support facility" that would be collocated with the Air Force program offices responsible for systems development. [32]

After much debate inside the Air Force, the changes suggested by the Winter Study Group eventually came to pass. In the summer of 1961, the Air Force formed a new organization at headquarters, Air Force Systems Command, that included an Electronic Systems Division (ESD) at Hanscom Field. Research and development of existing and future L-Systems became the new division's primary responsibility. At the same time, MITRE became ESD's principal technical advisor.

In its new and larger role, MITRE supported the Air Force in the development of numerous electronic command and control systems during the 1960s. The work consisted of several specific responsibilities:

- assisting the military in the definition of system requirements;

- design and engineering of the complete system, with special emphasis on capability, integration, performance, reliability, and survivability;

- technical support during the acquisition of key components and subsystems, including technical review and evaluation of proposals and participation in design reviews; and

- testing and evaluation of the assembled system. [33]

These arrangements required the company to work closely not only with its customer, but also with private contractors. The company's status as a Federal Contract Research Center (FCRC)—it was not motivated by profit, did not compete for work, and protected the integrity of proprietary information—was a necessary part of establishing trusted relationships with all parties.[34]

31. Howard R. Murphy, *The Early History of The MITRE Corporation: Its Background, Inception, and First Five Years* (controlled distribution typescript publication, June 30, 1972 [copy at MITRE Corporation archives]), 177 and 210.

32. *The MITRE Corporation: The First Twenty Years*, 35; John F. Jacobs, *The SAGE Air Defense System: A Personal History* (Bedford, Mass.: The MITRE Corporation, 1986), 161.

33. MITRE Corporation, *Annual Report for 1963*.

34. MITRE's designation as an FCRC was changed to the more familiar name of Federally Funded Research and Development Center (FFRDC) in 1990.

Facing page:

In its first Annual Report in 1962, MITRE explained its role in systems development using a simple but clear graphic illustration.

In return for its services, the Air Force paid MITRE for its direct costs, and provided a modest "fee-for-need" that enabled the company to build or rent facilities in Bedford, Washington, and branch locations, and supported the company's small independent research and development (IR&D) program. Although some critics considered MITRE's IR&D as an extravagance, customers agreed to support it because it helped keep the company's technical staff abreast of fast-moving developments in core technologies in sensors, data processing, and communications.

MITRE's programs and projects for the Air Force during the early 1960s reflected the defense priorities of the era and involved assignments in air defense, strategic and tactical air support, and warning and defense against missile attacks. The company's major engagements during the early 1960s included:

Air Defense

■ the follow-on to SAGE, a program called the Backup Interceptor Control (BUIC), which replaced the vacuum-tube computers of the original program with new machines featuring solid-state components and placed them in dispersed locations to help ensure survivability;

■ adaptations of SAGE and BUIC for Europe, Japan, and eventually Vietnam;

■ the Airborne Long-Range Input (ALRI), a program to mount air defense radars in aircraft patrolling the North American coasts.

Strategic and Tactical Systems

■ the computer and communications systems at the headquarters of the Strategic Air Command in Omaha;

■ the Tactical Air Control System (407L), a mobile system of radars, communications equipment, and control centers that on short notice could be airlifted into combat zones and quickly made operational.

Early Warning/Missile Defense

■ the computer and communications systems in NORAD's Combat Operations Center at Cheyenne Mountain, Colorado.

Although the Air Force remained by far MITRE's biggest customer, the company also began working for other defense agencies during the early 1960s. These assignments reflected a growing demand for information systems that crossed the boundaries of the military services and integrated their respective command and control systems. The biggest and most significant program of this kind was the National Military Command System (NMCS), which combined "all the facilities, equipment, doctrine, procedures, and communications" required by the President, the Secretary of Defense, and the Joint Chiefs of Staff to direct the nation's armed forces. This program originated in the aftermath of the Cuban missile crisis, when the President's ability to command and control America's military forces in the event of a nuclear attack became a major strategic consideration. The survivability of communications capability was a particular concern, and early conceptions of the NMCS featured multiple command centers, including hardened facilities and airborne platforms, and redundant equipment and systems.

Responsibility for systems engineering and technical supervision of the NMCS fell to the Defense Communications Agency (DCA), an entity inside the Department of Defense that represented all three branches of the military. In October 1963, the DCA selected MITRE as its principal source of technical support for the NMCS. In explaining the award, the agency cited MITRE's strong track record in developing command and control systems for the Air Force and its objectivity as an FCRC. That fall, Charles Zraket moved from Bedford along with several dozen colleagues to new quarters outside Washington, D.C. as head of a new division, MITRE (DCA). This group soon joined with the MITRE contingent working for the FAA to establish the company's Washington Operations.[35]

35. MITRE Corporation, MITRE: The First Twenty Years, pp. 70-71; MITRE Corporation, Annual Report for 1964, Charles Zraket interview, October 22, 1997.

Counter Air

Search and Rescue

Air Refueling

Carrier Fleet Early Warning

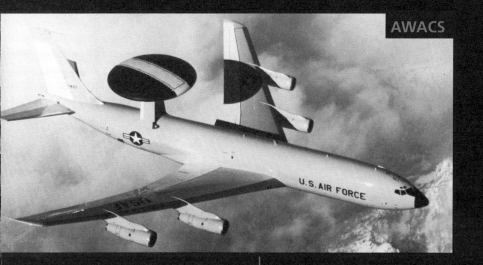
AWACS

Case Two: **The Sentry**

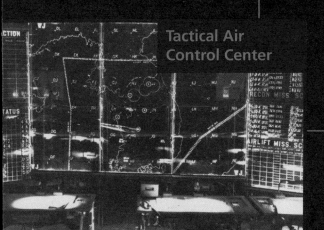
Tactical Air
Control Center

Ground Surveillance

The Airborne Warning and Control System (AWACS) uses sophisticated radar and communications equipment to sense aircraft at great distances and report this information to military commanders. The system extends the range of ground-based radars by hundreds of miles and enables early detection of enemy threats.

MITRE began supporting AWACS development at the program's inception in the mid-1960s. Since then, the company has worked on many upgrades and improvements to the system. Originally conceived to supplement SAGE along coastal areas, AWACS evolved into a mobile tactical system to support projection of U.S. forces overseas. Today the system not only remains a vital component of American military superiority but also is used extensively by U.S. allies.

Pictured on overleaf: AWACS relays its radar picture of distant skies to military forces on the ground, air, or sea.

The Sentry

The expanding scope of MITRE's work during the early 1960s reflected not only concerns about proliferating and incompatible electronic systems that the Winter Study Group had identified, but also a dramatic shift in thinking about national defense. SAGE had been conceived during an era in which the gravest threat to the United States was a large, coordinated bomber attack. By the early 1960s, however, times and technology had changed. The most dangerous threat was now the intercontinental ballistic missile, and SAGE—or any other technology of the era—was powerless to protect against it. At the same time, there was growing unease in the defense community about the doctrine of "massive retaliation," which called for the nation to deter attack with the threat of a huge, destructive counterattack. To the new Kennedy administration, it seemed more likely that the country would be drawn into smaller, more dispersed conflicts unsuited to massive retaliation. Accordingly, the administration developed a new doctrine under the rubric of "flexible response." As the name indicated, the new doctrine called for the capability for quick actions, perhaps many of them at once, tailored to specific circumstances.

For the Air Force and MITRE, flexible response entailed less emphasis on continental air defense and more on developing new strategic and tactical command and control systems. The fate of the Airborne Warning and Control System (AWACS) illustrates this shift of emphasis. Originally conceived as an airborne early warning system to complement and extend SAGE's radar coverage, AWACS instead evolved into a mobile command and control platform that could be dispatched to distant battlefields. With its distinctive profile, a Boeing 707 with a rotating radome perched upon the fuselage, AWACS eventually became a symbol of American technological and military superiority—as illustrated in its role in the 1991 Gulf War, when the system helped monitor enemy air traffic and coordinated the thousands of sorties flown each day by Coalition aircraft.

Today, it is impossible to imagine an American military engagement occurring without support from these sophisticated sentries. Yet in mid-1966, when MITRE began working on the original performance specifications, supporters were few and critics had strong doubts about the value of such a system given the changing Soviet threat. At the same time, there was serious disagreement within the U.S. military about the design of the system in light of the different needs of the Air Force and the Navy. Only in the mid-1970s, following a convincing demonstration in which MITRE personnel and MITRE-developed systems played key roles, did the Department of Defense finally decide to include AWACS in its arsenal of essential weapon systems.

Origins

AWACS emerged from two separate streams of development: work originally sponsored by the Navy during World War II to complement and extend shipboard radar, and Air Force programs to apply principles and technology from SAGE to airborne radar systems. These separate streams began to merge in the mid-1960s.

36. Henry E. Guerlac, *Radar in World War II*. 2 vols. (New York: Tomash, 1987 [1946]), 1:537. Detection was but part of the Navy's response. The other was the development of guided missiles which would "lock-on" and destroy attacking kamikaze aircraft. This development, Project Bumblebee, was spearheaded by Merle Tuve and his staff at the Johns Hopkins University Applied Physics Laboratory in Silver Spring, Maryland.

The Navy's interest in long-range radars intensified during the late stages of World War II in the Pacific, when the Service encountered a new enemy weapon, the kamikaze. The Japanese quickly learned that by flying under the coverage of the shipboard radar they would increase the deadly efficacy of their suicide attacks. For the Navy, the best defense was obvious—extend the range of shipboard radar over the horizon.[36] Researchers at MIT's Radiation Laboratory, one of MITRE's technological ancestors, identified a quick, but far from easy solution: connect an airborne early warning radar with a ship's combat information center. What became Project Cadillac at the Rad Lab was among the most sophisticated and expensive wartime research programs, absorbing 12 percent of the laboratory's budget and demanding the development of components for both the airborne radar and the ship-borne system. Furthermore, differentiating between friendly and enemy aircraft necessitated the invention of the IFF (Identification Friend or Foe) systems which are still in use today—systems which allow radar operators to identify the friendly, equipped aircraft from otherwise anonymous blips on their radar screens.

After 13 months of intensive work on concurrent research, development, and production schedules, the Rad Lab delivered the first functional units in March 1945. Although the system was successful, its initial defects were considerable. First, the airborne system, whose bulbous radars were contained in a bulge between the landing gear, consumed so much space and power that the Grumman TBM-3W Avenger, the Navy's carrier-based torpedo plane, could have only a one man crew. All radar processing was done on the ships receiving the plane's data. Hence, Cadillac became an extension of the ship's radar, but not an independent observer capable of directing battle. Cadillac II, begun during the war, attempted to solve this problem by converting a B-17G Flying Fortress into a flying combat information center, with multiple radar consoles and radar operators capable of communicating with any ship within radio range. Designed to assist in the coordination of the vast fleet necessary for an invasion of the Japanese home islands, Cadillac II was never deployed in combat. However, the lessons learned were absorbed by the Navy, which continued the development of the system during the 1950s.

Central to Cadillac and its progeny was the development of radar systems capable of detecting an object amid ground and sea clutter. Although this might sound like a simple problem, it lay at the core of developing AWACS. Separating ocean and aircraft reflections was accomplished with much effort during World War II through research on the "Moving Target Indicator."[37] The Navy sponsored the continuing refinement of this technology throughout the postwar period, leading to the deployment of a land-based Lockheed Constellation with an improved moving target indication system. Beginning in 1951, the Air Force also purchased this plane, calling it the E-121C Warning Star, to extend radar coverage over the ocean approaches to the continental United States.

Despite the Navy's success in developing radars capable of distinguishing ocean from aircraft, these same radars were unable to separate out ground clutter from low-flying aircraft. Compared to the ever changing topography of land, the ocean was a relatively stable reflector. By the mid-1950s, the Navy's research had extended to cover the problem of viewing aircraft above land as well as water. The technology, the airborne moving-target indicator, worked by comparing successive radar returns and subtracting the sections of each return which remained constant. In theory, the reflections left would relate to moving objects only. General Electric was the lead Navy developer of this system, but a central problem confronting them was the processor-intensive character of the moving target indicator. No plane could carry something equivalent to a Whirlwind II computer. Only in 1964 did the Navy finally deploy the Grumman E-2A Hawkeye, the result of their extensive R&D effort. The problem of ground clutter remained, but Air Force research directors believed that the use of the Navy's moving target technology or a novel radar technology, pulse doppler, might resolve the issue. To facilitate a solution, the Air Force created the Overland Radar Technology (ORT) development program and let contracts for partial prototypes to Raytheon, Westinghouse, and Hughes.[38] Based on flight tests, Hughes and Westinghouse were chosen as candidate suppliers for the AWACS radar. For the Air Force, the attraction of the program was the potential of using the SAGE system, or some derivative of that project, for tactical as well

37. See Guerlac, *Radar in World War II*, 615–617 on Moving Target Indication research at the Radiation Laboratory during the war.

38. See Jack Shay and Brent Hosage, "Introduction," in *MITRE and AWACS: A Systems Engineering Perspective* (Bedford, Mass.: The MITRE Corporation, 1990) 6.

as continental defense. In Vietnam, the Air Force used the EC-121C (also known as College Eye), to monitor the bombing of targets in North Vietnam, to help ensure that borders with China were respected, and to look out for enemy planes. Unable to distinguish aircraft from ground clutter, the EC-121C operated at low altitudes and directed its radar upwards, providing previously unavailable radar coverage. An Air Force program of the early 1960s, the Airborne Long-Range Input (ALRI), applied technology and lessons from SAGE to overcome some of the deficiencies of the EC-121C. Successful demonstration of the EC-121C and ALRI systems became the justification for a bigger development program in AWACS.[39]

AWACS was intended to replace the EC-121C and ALRI aircraft. However, it was one thing to declare a successor, another to design and build such a complicated system. Beyond the obvious difficulties of constructing what was an airborne SAGE control center, there were technical and operational problems that designers had to address, challenge, and discipline—all before building the coalition necessary to acquire the Congressional support for what would become a multi-billion dollar program. Among the technical problems were several basic questions: First, would the AWACS radar work and discriminate ground clutter from moving targets? Second, would AWACS work in a world of electronic counter-measures designed to deceive its radar while using electronic counter-countermeasures to display enemy aircraft? Would AWACS wind up jamming itself? Third, could AWACS, based in a modified Boeing 707, survive in battle? Wouldn't the AWACS become a prime target for an enemy? Finally, was AWACS even necessary? Why not use the Navy's E-2C, the Hawkeye, which worked over water? Given that AWACS initial justification was continental air defense, Congressional opponents declared it useless against Soviet ballistic missiles; or as Senator John Stennis observed: "the need for continental defense [was] on a par with the need for a new stone catapult."[40]

From Requirements to Demonstration

By 1966 the Overland Radar Technology development program reached a point where the Electronic Systems Division of the Air Force Systems Command commissioned MITRE to produce a statement of work for the command, control and communications (C^3) functions of AWACS. Jack Dominitz, Hank Therrien, Ed Gallivan, Walt Charow, and others drafted the detailed statement of work which articulated in detail which topics and areas needed to be examined in order to produce a performance system specification. The specification, developed in conjunction with the system contractor teams, in this case Boeing and McDonnell Douglas, would identify and delineate AWACS C^3 capabilities. In other words, the system requirements were a textual AWACS, a representation that contractors

The predecessors of AWACS included the Airborne Long-Range Input (ALRI), pictured here at the Naval Air Station in South Weymouth, Massachusetts.

39. The MITRE Corporation, *MITRE: The First Twenty Years* (Bedford, Mass.: The MITRE Corporation, 1978), 115–116.

40. *MITRE and AWACS*, 8.

would implement in the equipment they would build. Unfortunately for MITRE, neither contractor had a full sense of what an AWACS would actually need. Put simply, AWACS needed to be the equivalent of a ground SAGE control center, but this was a physical impossibility. Originally, MITRE was to take the initial reports from the contractors and begin the process of creating a final performance specification, one that took into account the needs of two different customers within the Air Force—Air Defense Command and Tactical Air Command.

By October 1966 it became clear that the contractors' reports would be of less help than expected in producing the final performance specification. The MITRE AWACS team, under the unofficial leadership of Gerry Langelier, realized that they would have to draft the entire report.[41] Given MITRE's background in air defense this was not an absolute calamity, but it was well outside of the original plan. Putting the specification together required that the team clearly delineate the performance, but not the actual design, of each AWACS functional component. Furthermore, this delineation demanded quantitative foundations and mechanisms to test the system. Testing and specification writing went hand in hand at MITRE.

41. See Gerry Langelier, "Building the Specification," in *MITRE and AWACS*, 12-21.

Below:

The Boeing 707 aircraft that originally carried AWACS aloft bristled with high tech equipment and systems.

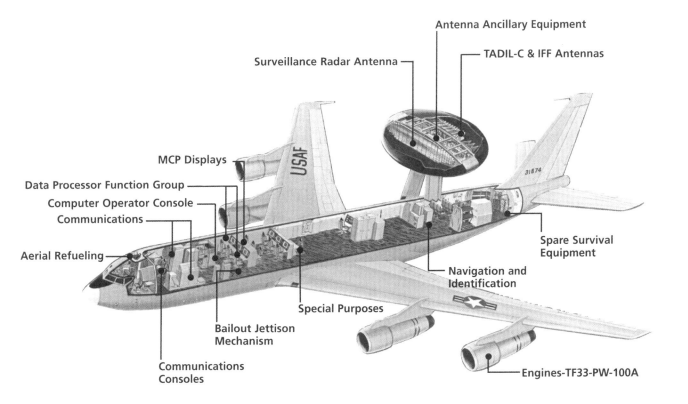

Antenna Ancillary Equipment

TADIL-C & IFF Antennas

Surveillance Radar Antenna

MCP Displays

Data Processor Function Group

Computer Operator Console

Communications

Aerial Refueling

Spare Survival Equipment

Navigation and Identification

Special Purposes

Bailout Jettison Mechanism

Communications Consoles

Engines-TF33-PW-100A

MITRE delivered the AWACS C³ performance specification to the Electronics System Division on Valentine's Day 1967. In turn, ESD transmitted the report to the Aeronautical Systems Division (ASD), headquarters of AWACS development. In March, the Air Force asked for a complete performance specification, including the airframe and avionics, within two months. As work proceeded, it became clear that the sensor and command-and-control issues were dominant over the aircraft integration effort, and ESD became the division responsible for the AWACS specification and MITRE its partner in the enterprise. After six revisions, and minor suggestions from the various Air Force Commands, the final specification appeared in May 1968.

The end of the performance specification phase did not lead smoothly into the contract definition phase where McDonnell Douglas, Boeing, and their respective teams of subcontractors would develop "low level specifications, management plans, and costs."[42] Instead, the Air Force found itself without the funds to pay for the next phase of AWACS. Without funding, the contractors would not be able to retain their employees, the very people who could build the proposed technology. To keep the contractors whole, MITRE pushed for a low-level, one-year, radar support program which provided funds for research on a variety of AWACS technology. Hughes and Westinghouse, the two major radar subcontractors, did extensive, pathbreaking work on the development of radar transmitters, while the airframe manufacturers worked on radome modeling. What began as a last-ditch means of preserving organizations and technical talent became vital to the ultimate success of the program. MITRE's actions reflected its realization that without the contractors, all the work on the performance specification would have been lost.

42. See Bill Canty, "The Brassboard Program," in *MITRE and AWACS,* 24–33, 32.

In the summer of 1970, the Department of Defense announced that Boeing would be the lead AWACS contractor. In turn, Boeing would select the radar contractor after a flyoff between two competing designs, one from Hughes, the other from Westinghouse. Each radar contractor would build a full-scale example of its design; each would be mounted in a separate airplane and then tested thoroughly, especially in its ability to detect low-flying fighter aircraft over various terrains. After interpreting the test results and determining which radar was best suited for the mission, Boeing would seek the Air Force's approval of its decision. This phase, known as the Brassboard Program, allowed the Air Force to understand AWACS strengths and weaknesses before making a production decision. Furthermore, during the Brassboard Program, MITRE would actively work to identify new missions and find new users for this multi-billion dollar technology. Any decision to produce AWACS would demand the building of an alliance among contractors, users, and consultants to persuade Congress of the system's value.

The stakes of the Brassboard Program were huge. For the two radar contractors, Hughes and Westinghouse, much money was on the line. Whichever radar system approach won would provide substantial business to its respective company. For Boeing, it was essential that at least one of the radar subcontractors produce a working radar that would solve the problem of distinguishing aircraft from ground clutter. For MITRE, the stakes were nothing short of its identity and relationship with the Air Force. As the AWACS general system engineer, MITRE was responsible for insuring that firms did not produce flawed designs or technologies that would not meet the performance specifications. Also, MITRE was responsible for developing the elaborate testing program that would make it possible to choose between the two radar designs, as well as the testing that would demonstrate the prototype AWACS aircraft's ability to meet the pre-existing specifications. Finally, AWACS was the company's first truly big project since SAGE; a "working" AWACS was more than a system of very high complexity, it would serve as a symbol of MITRE's expertise and maturity.[43]

Hughes and Westinghouse each had offered a promising technology in the Overland Radar Technology Program. Hughes chose to develop a medium-PRF (pulse radio frequency) doppler radar, and Westinghouse worked on a high-PRF doppler radar. MITRE's role involved learning the design philosophies of the radar contractors and how each company would try to meet the performance specification. The existing radar expertise within MITRE allowed the firm to develop sophisticated computer models for testing each radar's capabilities. Computer modeling allowed MITRE engineers to predict problems so that designers would recognize the limitations of their designs. Experimental work conducted by MITRE at Hanscom Air Force Base also produced data to use in judging radar design and effectiveness.

In addition to working with the radar contractors, MITRE advocated Boeing's early involvement in the design of the AWACS radome. No matter how effective the radar system chosen, an inadequate radome would render AWACS incapable of operating at its full effectiveness. Under the radome's cover, the radar would emit the electromagnetic waves; it was important that the radome be as transparent as possible so as not to degrade or distort either the outgoing or incoming signal. At the same time, the radome had to be designed so that it would not affect the performance of the Boeing 707 underneath it. Labeled an "insult to aerodynamics," the AWACS radome became the aircraft's most distinctive external feature.[44]

43. William Canty interview, October 7, 1997.

44. Canty, "The Brassboard Program," 31.

MITRE also played another key role in AWACS, acting as an information manager for the entire project. Trip reports and monthly project reviews prepared by the AWACS system engineers became required reading throughout the management of the Air Force System Program Office (SPO), that was responsible for the program. Brigadier General Kendall Russell, head of the Air Force AWACS System Program Office at Hanscom AFB was a regular reader, as was the General Accounting Office. The circulation of these reports performed several important functions. First, the reports allowed all the readers to be "on the same page" with respect to AWACS development. Second, the reports enhanced MITRE's role in AWACS development. To keep abreast of development, the reports were essential reading. Third, by synthesizing information from various sites—including Hughes, Westinghouse, and Boeing—MITRE created communications among the developers necessary for the program's success, and uncovered communications failures early enough to permit timely fixes. In a sense, MITRE became more than the AWACS systems engineer; MITRE and AWACS became inextricably intertwined.

By Spring 1971, the Brassboard Program was well under way and the flight testing was to be the next major activity. Seattle, Boeing's home base, would become the center of AWACS activity. Rather than attempt to engineer AWACS from across the continent, MITRE set up an office in Seattle to provide on-the-ground advice and technical support during a series of ground test evaluations and as the radars were moved into the test aircraft. The Seattle operation was an extension of MITRE's Bedford capabilities; problems and analyses flowed easily through phone lines and other communication links.

Standing inside an AWACS E-3A aircraft at Hanscom Field are (l. to r.) Brigadier General Robert L. Edge, ESD Commander Major General Albert R. Shiely Jr., Bob Everett, and Brigadier General Kendall Russell.

45. Ibid., 29.
46. Ibid., 30.

Site Leader Bill Canty ran the 12-person shop. Its initial work centered on the development of the flight test program. Designing a rigorous and credible testing series was Boeing's job, but Canty believed that if MITRE did such work independently, the systems engineers would be in a better position to understand and improve Boeing's testing plan. Furthermore, independent development would provide a useful way to defend the tests if they were later attacked on the basis that Boeing had defined tests that it believed the system could easily pass.

By January 1972, Hughes and Westinghouse had their radar systems nearly ready for the trip to Seattle. Although MITRE engineers would have preferred that the systems remain in their respective factories until the units met all the requirements, the contractors and the Air Force SPO director, Brigadier Kendall General Russell, believed that whatever problems remained could be fixed as the systems were readied for flight testing.[45] The MITRE counterargument had been simple, but ineffective. If the contractors waited to ship the systems until they met the specifications, they could use their time in Seattle to address the unforeseen and inevitable problems that would emerge during the next phase. And problems would occur.

After the arrival of the Westinghouse and Hughes radar systems in Seattle, along with their respective teams of engineers and technicians, the systems were placed in full-scale mockups of the aircraft and tested as to their ability to meet the specifications, given the ground-based restrictions. Boeing created separate teams to work with each radar contractor and made it clear that there was to be no communication between Boeing employees working on the rival systems. Communication of knowledge between Hughes and Westinghouse could jeopardize the outcome of the tests, as well as each firm's competitive position, and open up the final decision to litigation. Boeing wanted MITRE and the Air Force to assign discrete, non-communicating groups to each contractor; MITRE had neither the manpower nor the resources in its Seattle office to do as Boeing suggested. Despite this inability to provide structural secrecy for the contractors, there was never any doubt among any of the contractors that Canty's engineers had been anything less than totally honest and uncompromising in their work with each company.[46] This was significant as it became another source of credibility, enabling the MITRE engineers to make changes in the testing program that might otherwise have been impossible.

By February 1972, Boeing had delivered the aircraft for the flight tests; Hughes and Westinghouse installed their systems in their respective planes. After several shakedown flights the AWACS radar flyoff began in late March. Initial radar results were expected to be poor, but by May neither radar system was operating at the agreed upon 60 percent of the performance specification. Indeed, Boeing and MITRE agreed that the systems were only working at 40 to 45 percent of the specification. After much deliberation MITRE's Jack Shay delivered the news to the Air Force. The radar technology was not working as well as intended; if the Air Force allowed each contractor to make changes to their system it was far more likely that at least one of the techniques would meet the specification. Boeing seconded this opinion; the Air Force halted flight testing for May and June. Hughes and Westinghouse used the time to make important changes in their equipment.

When flight testing resumed in late June the radar performance on each aircraft was dramatically improved. Canty's group advocated the use of actual F-4 fighters rather than simulated signals to make part of the tests more realistic. With the design and testing data and much negotiation, MITRE and Boeing produced a final

report and recommendation by mid-September. By October 1, the AWACS SPO had read and approved the report—the Westinghouse system was clearly superior. The MITRE engineers, particularly Herb Feldman, still believed that Boeing needed to work on the radome; it was a problem that would not go away. However, the Brassboard program had proven the possibility of an airborne radar capable of tracking aircraft against the earth's surface. Boeing was ready to let the subcontracts, but there was one serious problem: there was still no agreement that the nation needed AWACS.

Persuasion and Production

Technical feasibility was not identical with political reality. For AWACS to proceed to production, the Air Force SPO, Boeing, and MITRE would have to persuade other parts of the Air Force and the other Services of the value of the system. This meant more than distributing the final Brassboard report; it meant showing different prospective users how AWACS might benefit them so that they would become advocates of the system. MITRE played an extraordinary part in the process of persuasion, developing both the context and the technologies that convinced others of AWACS' importance. MITRE's main idea was really quite simple: a road trip. In April 1973, the Brassboard AWACS plane flew to Europe to demonstrate its capabilities to NATO members. This was not simply a demonstration of the radar's ability to track aircraft in a large surveillance volume; it became a demonstration of the power of information in and on the future battlefield. In particular, the European tests made it clear that AWACS would be of immense value in any struggle against the Warsaw Pact.

The source of the demonstration's power lay in MITRE's decision to integrate another novel technology into AWACS. With a new MITRE AWACS project leader, Jack Shay, fresh from MITRE's tactical work in Vietnam, AWACS acquired a much stronger tactical focus. This was due as much to the Soviet use of ballistic missiles which rendered continental defense somewhat less important as it was to the recognition that AWACS could have powerful implications for a tactical operational theater. In particular, Shay wanted to bring MITRE's Seek Bus technology to AWACS.

Seek Bus was an early version of the Joint Tactical Information Distribution System (JTIDS) discussed later in this book (*Case 3*), and it helped to transform a sophisticated flying radar system into a major command, control, communication, and intelligence (C^3I) system. Encrypted and jam-resistant, Seek Bus broadcast information which receivers could selectively monitor, depending upon

Facing page:

AWACS development received a boost from another MITRE-engineered system called Seek Bus (later known as the Joint Tactical Information Distribution System). Seek Bus increased the power of AWACS by broadcasting additional information about aircraft to friendly pilots and commanders.

need and interest. An AWACS with Seek Bus, for example, might broadcast a data-set containing information about an aircraft's altitude and heading as well as information about other aircraft it was tracking. Soldiers in a surface-to-air missile battery could set their receivers to pick up information about potential targets still invisible to their ground-based radar.

Seek Bus consisted of special transmitters, receivers, and terminals that allowed for the communication of tactical information on a need-to-know basis that allowed not only for the integration of different technical systems, but of rival Services. The AWACS could provide information to Army missile batteries, Navy ships, and NATO allies. Seek Bus gave AWACS even greater potential and prospective value. There was only one problem—Seek Bus was still under development as the European demonstration was being planned. Seek Bus would have to work its first time out of the box for the demonstration to be as effective as planned by Shay, Canty, and others.[47]

47. On the European demonstration, see Maurice Vacherot and William Canty, "The European Demonstration," in *MITRE and AWACS*, 36-43; on Seek Bus and JTIDS, see Eric Ellingson, "The European Demonstration: A JTIDS Perspective," in *MITRE and AWACS*, 46-53; and C. Kenneth Allard, *Command, Control, and the Common Defense* (New Haven: Yale University Press, 1990),189-240.

Proving the value of the Seek Bus and AWACS technologies to General David C. Jones, Commander-in-Chief of U.S. Air Forces Europe, became top priorities of the demonstrations. In particular, MITRE engineers and technical analysts produced studies demonstrating the AWACS combat survivability and the integration of aerial surveillance with ground forces such as surface-to-air missile batteries. The survivability of the AWACS Boeing 707 aircraft in operational conditions had always been a question brought up by AWACS critics. After much study, MITRE analysts concluded that AWACS would have a high probability of survival in a combat situation. Given the distance the craft could search, it would require a very coordinated attack to destroy the AWACS, especially in Europe where the craft would always be operating in friendly air space. In other words, it was possible that an AWACS could be destroyed by a sufficiently determined attacker, but such attacks were difficult to coordinate and the loss of an AWACS was a low probability event. Furthermore should an AWACS be lost, it could readily be replaced on orbit by back-up aircraft. While these studies were important to Jones, it was the experience of flying aboard the Brassboard plane in the United States that converted him into a champion of the new technology. In particular, the Seek Bus technologies captured his imagination. Jones invited Russell to bring the Seek Bus-enhanced AWACS to Europe in April 1973 to demonstrate its ability to work with NATO air, land, and sea forces.

The importance of the successful European tests cannot be underestimated. Within three months, MITRE built Seek Bus transmitters and terminals and installed them at test locations in Europe. Furthermore, MITRE also integrated the new technology into the Brassboard AWACS. Finally, MITRE had to make the Seek Bus terminals interface with existing NATO technology which was far from standardized.

However, that was part of the demonstration's success. Observers in Ramstein, West Germany, were able to see the air space of an AWACS on station above the Adriatic Sea. For the commanders, the radar screen had become an accurate representation of the battlefield's dynamic characteristics, and they were convinced of AWACS' value. Furthermore, the new technology acquired another set of powerful champions capable of defending and explaining the reasons why the nation needed to invest in this program.

Despite the success of the European tests and the enthusiasm of NATO for AWACS, Congress remained unconvinced. Amid growing opposition to U.S. involvement in the Vietnam War and the Watergate scandal, there was considerable public skepticism about military technology and the value of investing in big new programs. The Washington Post opined against funding AWACS, and Senator Thomas Eagleton of Missouri blasted the system as a waste because of its inability to help defend against a Soviet missile attack. He argued that the Air Force could instead use the Navy's already existing Hawkeye aircraft. Rebutting Eagleton and other critics required more flight testing of the Brassboard aircraft to demonstrate its relative invulnerability to enemy electronic countermeasures and more studies on the issue of survivability. MITRE researchers played a major role in these studies.

At the same time, Defense Secretary James Schlesinger was also concerned about the Air Force's continuing view of AWACS as a tool for continental air defense. Rather, Schlesinger urged the Service to redefine AWACS as a mobile tactical system for primary use overseas. Later he recalled saying to the Air Force, "Modify the aircraft so that we can send it overseas. By the way, this would mean that the Air Force could compete with the Navy in terms of maintaining a U.S. presence abroad." Schlesinger also saw AWACS as helping to bolster NATO defenses against the offensive capabilities of the Warsaw Pact.[48]

48. James Schlesinger interview, June 8, 1998.

In August 1974, at the request of the Senate Armed Services Committee, Schlesinger appointed a panel of independent experts to assess the ability of AWACS to perform its functions under battle conditions. Known as the Smith Committee, because of its chairman, Harold Smith, Jr., a professor of applied science at the University of California, the panel produced scenarios that required MITRE to generate reports demonstrating the AWACS capabilities. These reports proved vital to the committee's final recommendation that AWACS was a necessary and important part of the nation's defense. The committee's final report allowed Schlesinger to furnish the Senate with the guarantees necessary to approve AWACS production.

Sentries on Station

The first E-3 AWACS aircraft went on station in 1977 under the 552nd Air Control Wing at Tinker Air Force Base. In the ensuing decades, the Air Force acquired 30 more E-3s, while forces representing NATO, Saudi Arabia, England, France, and Japan purchased another 38 aircraft. The technology at the heart of AWACS has been upgraded repeatedly to take account of faster computers, more sensitive radars, and better equipment.[49] A quarter century after the first successful demonstrations, AWACS is still going strong: in March 1998, Japan took delivery of an upgraded system carried aloft aboard a Boeing 767.

AWACS has distinguished itself in dozens of operations and engagements around the world. Its initial use in an emergency situation occurred in 1979, when two E-3s, air crews, and support personnel based in Japan were relocated to the Middle East to monitor a border dispute between North and South Yemen. Since then, AWACS has afforded commanders unparalleled views of air space in many hot spots: during the Iran-Iraq war in the 1980s, four E-3s rotated on around-the-clock duty above Saudi Arabia for eight and a half years, monitoring the situation; in 1983 the 552nd Air Control Wing supported Operation Urgent Fury in Grenada; in 1986, AWACS aircraft were used to help interdict the flow of illegal drugs into the United States; and in 1989, AWACS supported Operation Just Cause in Panama.

The most conclusive public demonstration of AWACS occurred during the 1990–1991 crisis in the Persian Gulf, when the technology supported an air war that caused unparalleled devastation of targets in Iraq. AWACS aircraft not only warned Allied aircraft of enemy threats but also helped coordinate safely the massive amount of air traffic in the region each day during Desert Storm's air campaign.

The AWACS story shares a common element with the popular account of the Gulf War. There, the United States knitted together a coalition of allies to repulse Saddam Hussein's invasion of Kuwait and the threat his occupation posed to the world's oil supply. AWACS rested upon a similar network of allies who came together to support and develop a powerful technology. AWACS was as much this coalition of the Air Force, Boeing, Westinghouse, Congress, NATO and MITRE as it was an advanced technology. Supporting AWACS was simply another way in which MITRE demonstrated the power of a systems engineering process that encompassed not only hardware and software, but also the cultural and political institutions necessary to make them possible.

49. On the radome program see, Herb Feldman, "The Improved Radome Program," in *MITRE and AWACS*, 76-89.

Facing page:

The most distinctive feature of an AWACS aircraft is the radome housing the surveillance radar antenna. Labeled by some as "an insult to aerodynamics," the radome is a highly engineered product that must be fabricated with great care and precision.

1966 1967 1968

February 1
C. A. Zraket becomes vice president and head of newly formed Washington Operations

February 16
Washington Computer Center opens utilizing IBM 360/50

March 20
MITRE/NAFEC commences work on FAA design for future of air traffic control

April 10
Southeast Asia site opens

April 18
FAA dedicates National Aviation Facilities Experimental Center in Atlantic City

June 20
MITRE works on development on high-speed rail transportation

July
AWACS begins as MITRE project

July 1
C. W. Halligan retires: John L. McLucas becomes president

September 30
IBM 360/40 computer is installed in MITRE computer center

July 1
James R. Killian becomes chairman of the MITRE Board of Trustees

September 1
MITRE organizes TICCET computer-controlled television IR&D project

July 21
MITRE marks 10th Anniversary

November
Former MITRE Trustee Luis Alvarez wins Nobel Prize in Physics

November
Air Force lauds MITRE for "Outstanding Contributions to Joint Mission Analysis"

November 26
MITRE moves into Westgate Building (McLean, VA) (illustrated)

1 MITRE's own radar installation at its Bedford facility was affectionately known as "the golf ball."

2 In 1967 MITRE opened a facility in Atlantic City to support the FAA's National Aviation Facilities Experimental Center.

3 The following year, the company occupied the Westgate Building, its first major facility near Washington.

4 Among the company's new nondefense customers in the 1960s was NASA, where MITRE personnel supported systems for mission control.

4

January
Four MITRE Trustees —
Henry Loomis, Walter Roberts,
Jack Ruina, and Teddy
Walkowicz — become
advisors to President Nixon

January 15
First BUIC III facility is
dedicated

January 20
Richard M. Nixon is
inaugurated 37th President
of United States

February 18
Former MITRE President John
McLucas becomes Under
Secretary of Air Force

March
Jacksonville Florida, Air Route
Traffic Control Center begins
computer processing of flight
plans and weather data

March 26
Japanese BADGE air defense
system becomes operational

April 24
Robert R. Everett becomes
MITRE president

June
MITRE employee David Israel
(on leave to DOD) receives
Meritorious Civilian Service
Award

July 20
American astronauts Neil
Armstrong and Buzz Aldrin
walk on the moon

September
First nodes of ARPANET
(precursor of Internet)
become functional

September 26
Robert C. Sprague is named
chairman of MITRE Board of
Trustees

September 29
Brussels, Belgium site opens

February
President Nixon names
MITRE Trustee Dr. Gordon
J. F. MacDonald to newly
created Council on
Environmental Quality

April 22
Earth Day raises awareness
of environmental issues

May
MITRE supports FAA
implementation of Advanced
Flow Control Procedures to
relieve air traffic congestion
above New York City's major
airports

June
MITRE and the University
of Texas sponsor first
Interdisciplinary Conference
on Multiple Access Computer
Networks

July
Advanced Design and
Development Department
forms at Washington
Operations to handle new
FAA work

November
Initial tests of PLRACTA
antennas verify ability to
support two-way transmission
of digital data and measure
two-way range

January
MITRE increases work on
pollution and environmental
matters

January 13
Madrid, Spain site opens

March 1
National Science Foundation
awards grant to MITRE
to study computer-based
learning

June
MITRE begins work as
systems manager for Urban
Mass Transit Project

September
MITRE joins ARPANET

1972

1973

1974

1975

January
Altair 8800 personal
computer (first PC) is
introduced, retailing for $650

February 1
C. A. Zraket becomes senior
vice president, Technical
Operations

March
MITRE is awarded $4 million
contract to develop
computer-aided instruction

March
MITRIX local area network
is installed at Bedford

5

6

April
FAA and MITRE accelerate
efforts to complete
Automated Radar Terminal
System (ARTS III)

May 12
European Energy Symposium
is held in France

May 27
Magnetic Levitation
(MagLev) prototype train is
unveiled, completing Dept.
of Transportation project
with MITRE assistance

August
Law Enforcement Assistance
Association contract is
awarded to MITRE
Washington Operations

October 26
Robert A. Charpie is elected
chairman of the MITRE Board
of Trustees

October
Email introduced on the
ARPANET

April 30
AWACS/Seek Bus European
tests are completed

July
LINK GAT-1 air traffic
simulator is installed in
Washington

August 15
Langley, Virginia site opens

August 16
United Kingdom becomes
MITRE's first foreign air
traffic control client

October 9
MITRE Institute opens

December
OPEC oil embargo triggers
energy crisis

June 5
MITRE Interactive Terminal
System debuts in Washington

July
MITRE forms Energy
Resources and Environment
Division

July 1
Rome, New York site opens

August 9
President Nixon resigns.
Gerald R. Ford becomes
President of the United
States

August 23
IBM 370/158 computer
becomes operational in
Bedford

November 26
Patent awarded to MITRIX
Inventors

April 3
MITRE demonstates
AWACS/JTIDS to NATO
officials

August
Torrejon AFB, Spain site
opens

October 2
B Building in Bedford is
dedicated to C. W. "Hap"
Halligan

Interlude Two
Expanding Scope
1966–1976

June 1
Kaiserslautern, Germany
site opens

June 15
Undersecretary of Defense
Malcolm Currie submits
report on organization of
federal contract research
centers to Congress

June 16
MITRE hosts E-3A Seminar
at Bedford

5 Another civil systems
venture of the 1960s and
early 1970s was high-speed
trains featuring magnetic-
levitation technology

6 MITRE's Maury Vacherot,
Dave Willard, and Mike
Cogan (l. to r.) developed
and patented MITRIX,
a technology using coaxial
cable as a medium for
distributing digital
information.

7 Satellite antennae—like the
golf ball—festooned the
Bedford campus and
facilitated high-speed, high-
volume communications.

Expanding Scope, 1966–1976

In the spring of 1966, Hap Halligan announced his impending retirement from MITRE in a phased manner that called for him to relinquish the presidency in July while remaining for a transitional period on the board of trustees as chair of the executive committee. In searching for a new president, the board reached outside and elected 45-year-old John McLucas, a former aerospace industry executive who possessed significant experience in science administration and government affairs. McLucas had most recently completed a two-year stint as Assistant Secretary General for Scientific Affairs in NATO and previously had served as Deputy Director of Defense Research and Engineering.

An immediate challenge that McLucas faced was to manage MITRE's support to U.S. forces as the war in Vietnam escalated. The conflict affected the company's operations in significant ways, accelerating development of tactical programs such as 407L, a system of mobile radars and communications equipment that could be airlifted to distant locations and assembled quickly to provide air defense and air traffic control functions; and Seek Data II, an initiative to automate certain information-intensive activities such as planning air sorties and reporting daily statistics on operations. The war also tested and hastened development of MITRE-supported air defense systems including Combat Lightning, a series of modified back up interceptor control (BUIC) installations, and the Airborne Long-Range Input (ALRI), an airborne surveillance program that prepared the way for AWACS. Still another program involved designing and developing an "electronic fence" of sensors and communications devices to detect enemy infiltration and report it to friendly aircraft for interdiction. (*See Case 5.*)

50. MITRE Corporation, Annual Report for 1967.

To support these programs, MITRE opened an office in Bangkok and also dispatched personnel to Saigon and other locations in Southeast Asia.[50] In 1967, a quarter of MITRE's total effort was concentrated in Southeast Asia. The experience gained during the war proved invaluable to the company as it acquired first-hand knowledge of military field operations, tested its systems under combat conditions, and demonstrated its commitment and capabilities to the Air Force and other potential customers in the Department of Defense.

Another challenge facing McLucas was to manage the company's continuing work on strategic systems and its growing involvement in tactical systems in the context of tight budgets.[51] In 1964, Congress had set funding ceilings that restricted the amount of support the Air Force could obtain from MITRE and other Federal Contract Research Centers, and during the second half of that year, for the first time in the company's young life, its contract revenues from the Air Force declined.[52] MITRE's trustees and executives faced a genuine dilemma. Although the company's work for the Air Force was exciting, challenging, and important to the nation, its leaders became concerned with MITRE's future stability, including the effect of declining revenues on its capability to offer its technical staff rising incomes and attractive career development opportunities. In the long run, the company feared losing key employees and its ability to recruit top-notch personnel, and eroding its capabilities and skill base.

Such reasoning resonated with the Air Force, which warmed to the idea that other funding sources would help maintain MITRE's vitality. High-level DOD officials, including Secretary Clark Clifford, also considered it legitimate for the commercial and not-for-profit organizations engaged in defense work to transfer military technology to civilian and commercial markets. And a host of these organizations—Federal Contract Research Centers such as RAND, and industrial contractors such as TRW and Raytheon—did exactly that, seeking to apply systems engineering skills and techniques to build cheaper housing, provide better public transportation, and improve government operations generally.[53]

McLucas proved a staunch advocate of diversification and he enjoyed the enthusiastic support of MITRE's trustees. (He later speculated that the trustees chose him as president because he seemed more likely than internal candidates to raise the company's profile in Washington in the DOD and other government agencies. Perhaps because he lacked a past at MITRE, he was better able to consider it an entity independent from its Air Force sponsor.) McLucas believed that "there was a market for almost an unlimited amount of MITRE support to various [government] groups and departments." He also became "very active in pushing the… idea that MITRE should not be totally captive to the Air Force." He acknowledged that such views were controversial, and the Air Force's other principal FCRC, Aerospace Corporation, considered them heresy. Nonetheless, McLucas urged MITRE to have "other irons in the fire" and "a more balanced set of customers."[54]

Almost immediately, MITRE began seeking new customers through its Washington office. This effort was aided by an expanding role in support of the National Airspace System for the Federal Aviation Administration (see Case 6). Between 1966 and 1970, the number of technical staff working for the FAA

In 1966 John McLucas (r.), a former defense industry executive and high-level DOD official, succeeded Hap Halligan as MITRE's president.

51. John McLucas interview, November 3, 1997.

52. MITRE Corporation, Annual Report for 1964.

53. MITRE Corporation, *MITRE: The First Twenty Years*. (Bedford, Mass.: The MITRE Corporation, 1979), 120 and 125. David R. Jardini "Out of the blue yonder. The RAND Corporation's Diversification into Social Welfare Research, 1946–1968," (Ph.D diss., Carnagie Melon University, 1996): Davis Dyer, "The Limits of Technology Transfer: Civil Systems at TRW, 1965-1975," in Thomas P. Hughes and Agatha C. Hughes, eds., *Systems, Experts, and Computers* (book manuscript in review, 1998).

54. McLucas interview, November 3, 1997.

55. John Quilty interview, December 2, 1997; Charles Zraket interview, October 22, 1997.

56. MITRE Corporation, *MITRE: The First Twenty Years,* 124-126.

climbed from about 20 to 90. In 1966, MITRE also began working for the National Aeronautics and Space Administration, which engaged MITRE to assess the design and operation of the Apollo mission control center in Houston (now the Johnson Space Flight Center). From there, MITRE carried out a steady stream of projects for NASA, chiefly in the acquisition, support, and analysis of computer systems for mission control, simulation and training, and administrative applications.[55]

In 1967, McLucas facilitated MITRE's diversification by restructuring the company into two decentralized units. Jack Jacobs became vice president and head of Bedford Operations, where support to the Air Force's Electronic Systems Division still accounted for the bulk of the company's revenues and employment. Meanwhile, Charles Zraket (addressed, like many subjects at MITRE, as an acronym: "CAZ") was promoted to vice president and head of Washington Operations, which included support to the Defense Communications Agency, the FAA, and NASA.

The establishment of Washington Operations reflected the conviction among MITRE trustees and executives that business in the nation's capital was bound to boom, even under—or perhaps because of—the restricted terms under which the company operated. And this business would not necessarily entail work for the Department of Defense. Zraket set about his work with uncommon energy and enthusiasm. In 1966, MITRE's work for the DOD (primarily the Air Force) accounted for more than 95 percent of total funding (about $35 million), with the FAA and NASA responsible for the remainder (about $5 million); by 1970, more than fifteen percent of the company's total funding (approximately $45 million) originated in contracts with civilian government agencies.

Charles A. Zraket—CAZ—presided over the rapid buildup of MITRE's Washington Operations in the 1960s and 1970s.

The new work included studies and analyses for the U.S. Department of Commerce and Transportation on high-speed ground transportation, including investigations into new methods of propulsion—magnetic-levitation trains for example. At the same time, MITRE engineers investigated the implications of high-speed trains: construction and maintenance of precisely measured track, assurance of ride quality, obstacle detection, and possible social and economic impacts. From there, MITRE's work continued to branch out:[56]

■ a study for the Arms Control and Disarmament Agency on how new command-and-control systems might affect arms control and disarmament;

■ an analysis for the Office of Civil Defense of post-attack scenarios;

■ a project to update the medical information retrieval systems for the Department of Health, Education, and Welfare;

- an investigation for the Internal Revenue Service to support a major upgrade of the agency's data processing systems;

- an exploration for the U.S. Weather Service of new techniques for upper air sounding;

- projects for the constituent organizations of what would become the Environmental Protection Agency on mapping water pollution and sensor systems for measuring air pollution.

In February 1968, the trustees voted to amend MITRE's certificate of incorporation to remove language limiting the company's work exclusively to the federal government. This step permitted MITRE to accept contracts with state governments and agencies, foreign governments, and quasi-public institutions such as electric utilities. MITRE engineers were soon working for local public health and medical organizations, as well as law enforcement agencies on information systems, communications systems, and long-range planning. The common denominator of all this work was the company's experience in developing computer-based information systems, and its general systems analysis and design approach to technological problems.[57]

The attraction of MITRE to civilian government customers was the same as its appeal to the Air Force: its expertise in developing and integrating complex systems, its commitment to public service, and its reputation for high-quality work and objective advice. Although not formally subject to FCRC rules, MITRE performed its civilian government assignments under exactly the same terms as its work for its formal sponsor: it avoided jobs put out for competitive bid and it accepted other restrictions required of FCRCs.[58]

The growing volume of work for civilian government customers led MITRE in 1968 to relocate Washington Operations into new facilities at Westgate Research Park in McLean, Virginia. By then, Washington Operations employed nearly 500

57. MITRE Corporation, *MITRE: The First Twenty Years*, 126-127 and 135.

58. Lydia Thomas interview, November 4, 1997.

technical staff. Many of the new hires carried degrees in social sciences as well as the natural sciences and engineering disciplines.

59. Robert Everett interview, October 24, 1997.

60. Greeley chronicled these initiatives in an unpublished manuscript entitled, Not-for-Profit: My Non-Military Career at MITRE (Well Off the Beaten Track), March 10, 1998. See also MITRE Corporation, *MITRE: The First Twenty Years*, 135-136.

61. U.S. Congress, Office of Technology Assessment, *A History of the Department of Defense Federally Funded Research and Development Centers*, OTA-BP-ISS-157 (Washington, D.C.: U.S. Government Printing Office, June 1995), 34; MITRE Corporation, Annual Report for 1975.

Early in 1969, Secretary of Defense Melvin R. Laird nominated McLucas as Under Secretary of the Air Force, triggering another executive change at MITRE. The company's new president was 47-year-old Bob Everett, who had run the company's operations since its founding and previously had served as director of MITRE's forebear, Division 6 at Lincoln Laboratory. Everett had supported MITRE's diversification, and the company's expansion continued apace and opportunistically. "We saw the world full of information systems," he recalled. "Everybody used them," including "all the government agencies." It seemed only natural, then, for MITRE to serve these government customers. "I often thought of MITRE as a spring which had all these capabilities and customers and jobs," Everett added. "This spring was a resource that many customers could tap. It also bubbled out along the edges and attracted new customers. We encouraged MITRE people to go and find interesting things to learn and as they worked around, we kept track of them. If somebody looked like he was doing well, then we would give him help, people and money, and management attention."[59]

In the 1970s, the fastest-growing areas of new business for the company reflected growing national concerns with the environment and energy. The establishment of the Environmental Protection Agency in 1970 created the need for new systems to monitor the environment. At the same time, MITRE and other research institutions anticipated the coming energy crises and embarked on a series of studies on energy-related issues. This work accelerated after the 1973-1974 oil shock, when the company supported the Energy Research and Development Administration (later a key constituent of the Department of Energy) in preparing a national energy research and development plan. This work was managed by the Energy Resources and Environment Division of Washington Operations, a unit established in 1974 under Richard S. Greeley.[60]

In the mid-1970s, the diversification strategies of the DOD's FCRCs became a source of concern both to high officials in the Defense Department and to the Air Force. In fiscal 1975, non-DOD work accounted for more than a third of MITRE's $73 million in contract revenues; at the same time, MITRE's work for the Air Force constituted about 50 percent of the total.[61] Meanwhile, DOD had given the Air Force expanded responsibilities to develop new command-and-control systems. Top brass at the Pentagon and at Hanscom AFB required increased support from MITRE and worried that the company's attention could be diverted by its civilian work. Officials in the DOD saw a more general problem that MITRE and other diversified FCRCs might lose their focus on their original mission to help provide for the nation's security. Industry representatives also protested the privileged position of the FCRCs, arguing that these entities provided services that the private sector could deliver with equal or greater efficiency.

In June 1976, Malcolm R. Currie, DOD director of defense research and engineering, presented to Congress a review of the management of the FCRCs. Currie reaffirmed the benefit of these institutions in providing high quality technical assistance and policy advice, but pointed out that ceilings on funding had produced some adverse effects, including efficiency and morale problems, an occasional and dispiriting need to cope with budget cuts late in the year, and "vigorous" diversification strategies. He also noted arguments originating among industrial contractors that "the FCRCs are placed in a favorable competitive position for non-DOD work by their relatively stable and assured base of DOD work and the resulting acquired experience."

In response to these concerns, Currie recommended that Congress reexamine the fixed funding ceilings on the FCRCs' core national security work and urged the trustees of each institution to limit diversification. In MITRE's case, he proposed a structural separation between the work the company carried out as a DOD FCRC and its other activities, which would not be subject to FCRC rules and restrictions. In other words, this work would be managed in the same way as a competitive professional services firm would do it. MITRE's FCRC funding ceiling would be flexible and linked to the DOD budget for command, control, and communications, and its non-FCRC work would be administered through a new, structurally separate organization.[62]

Anticipating congressional debate on Currie's recommendations, MITRE undertook a reorganization on its own initiative. The company announced the formation of a new unit, the "Metrek" Division, as of August 1, 1976.[63] Metrek subsumed the non-DOD part of Washington Operations and became structurally separate from Bedford Operations, with its own cost accounting and internal management systems. Civilian government agencies engaging Metrek services contracted with MITRE directly, without reference to the company's sponsorship agreement with the Air Force.[64] At the same time, the restrictions on MITRE's ability to manufacture products, enter competitive bidding contests, or work for profit-making businesses, applied also to Metrek. MITRE applied these restrictions to Metrek although not legally required to do so by the DOD. It quickly became clear, however, that non-DOD customers valued MITRE's status as an FCRC and especially appreciated the objective quality of its advice and support.[65]

The growing volume of work in nondefense areas led MITRE to set up a new division called Metrek, with headquarters in northern Virginia.

62. Malcolm R. Currie, *Management of the Federal Contract Research Centers* (Washington, D.C.: U.S. Dept. of Defense, June 1976), 3-4, 6-8, and Attachment #1.

63. MITRE President Bob Everett coined the name "Metrek"; the name has no special meaning.

64. Thomas interview, November, 4, 1997.

65. MITRE Corporation, *MITRE: The First Twenty Years*, 254-255.

NATO AWACS

Joint Tactical Information Distribution System

AEGIS Cruiser

JTIDS-Equipped Carrier and Aircraft

F-15 Fighter Aircraft

Case Three

The JTIDS Journey

Missile Defense Battery

The Joint Tactical Information Distribution System (JTIDS) originated in the 1960s as a program to improve tactical situation awareness for pilots and air commanders. It evolved into a valuable tool that today helps dissipate "the fog of war" and minimize risks of errant friendly fire.

JTIDS rested on an original, MITRE-inspired concept of tactical communications. Developing the system entailed not only making significant technological advances but also achieving a new order of cooperation among the branches of the U.S. military.

Pictured on overleaf:
Visual representations of the information bus in the sky—also known as "the dog collar"—illustrates the cyclic information system at the heart of JTIDS. Information about position and status of friendly forces could be broadcast from and selectively received by a multitude of sources on the ground, at sea, or in the air, with continuous updating.

The JTIDS Journey

Dating from the late 1960s, the Joint Tactical Information Distribution System (JTIDS—pronounced "jaytids") is one of several MITRE projects in continuous development, operation, and evolution. As first conceived by the company, the system was designed to improve situation awareness for pilots and air commanders in tactical aerial combat. The underlying technology consisted of a secure, jam-resistant digital radio network that allowed the position and status of aircraft to be updated automatically and continuously, without having to interrogate transceivers. At the time, the new system promised to be a revolutionary way to create a much-needed capability—a robust, comprehensive air picture available in the fighter cockpit, tailored to each user's current needs. The system offered other attractive features, including self-location and positive friendly identification capabilities. Because the network was self-adaptive and did not depend on unique master stations, it could withstand the loss of any single aircraft or point source, or even a large number of casualties. At the same time, the system selectively processed information based upon each user's interests, so that a pilot could focus on particular kinds of information —pertinent, say, to the geographic sector in which the aircraft was flying or about to enter—while screening out less useful data. This concept, and the supporting technology, were considered revolutionary at the time.

Although the benefits of JTIDS seemed both obvious and compelling, the program ran up against a set of technological challenges and institutional barriers that impeded its implementation for many years. The long, twisting journey of JTIDS from concept to operation nonetheless illustrates several key lessons about MITRE's role as a systems architect and engineer for its government customers. First, the company can originate major programs as well as shape them once the customer has identified the mission. Second, MITRE possesses an ability to move quickly to design, test, and evaluate new functionality using off-the-shelf technology and equipment. Third, capabilities that radically modify operational concepts and procedures take a long time to take root. The company is able to work with the operational community over this time frame to help bring new capabilities into being. Finally, the institutional issues in implementing a new system can be as fraught with difficulty as the technological problems.

A member of the British team that cracked the Nazi Enigma code during World War II, Gordon Welchman outlined the basic principles of JTIDS in the mid-1960s.

66. Gordon Welchman, *The Hut Six Story: Breaking the Enigma Codes* (New York: McGraw-Hill Book Company, 1982). For Welchman's life and later career, see Nigel West, *The Sigint Secrets: The Signals Intelligence War, 1900 to Today—Including the Persecution of Gordon Welchman* (New York: William Morrow & Company, 1988), 25–28 and Appendix 3.

67. According to the company's official history, The MITRE Corporation, *MITRE: The First Twenty Years*. (Bedford, Mass.: The MITRE Corporation, 1979), 117. Welchman's work on battlefield communications originated in a MITRE-funded independent R&D study. Records of the IR&D program in the 1960s fail to mention either Welchman or his work. It seems more likely that his work was supported directly by the Air Force from a budget for long-range planning. However it was funded originally, the system that eventually became JTIDS clearly was inspired by Welchman and his colleagues at MITRE. Eric Ellingson interview, October 7, 1997.

68. Welchman, *The Hut Six Story*, 19–20.

69. Ibid., 256.

These lessons were not yet apparent in the mid-1960s, when top American defense officials continued their reassessment of strategic doctrine and some MITRE personnel began to ponder the role of communications on the outcome of battles throughout history.

Building a Bus in the Sky

In 1962, Bob Everett, MITRE's vice president for technical operations, enticed his old friend Gordon Welchman to join the company and assist in the development of tactical military systems. A native of the United Kingdom and a brilliant mathematician, Welchman had served during World War II as a senior staff member at Bletchley Park, where he worked with Alan Turing in the analysis of German coded communications.[66] After the war, Welchman emigrated to the United States. He landed first at MIT, where he joined Project Whirlwind. As director of applications research on Whirlwind, Welchman investigated many potential uses of real-time computer control, including civilian air traffic. In 1951, he left MIT to work in the fledgling computer industry, and he was at Itek Corporation 11 years later when the opportunity came to join MITRE.

In his new job, Welchman contributed to several tactical programs in development and also explored some open-ended questions such as the application of digital technology to battlefield communications.[67] This interest had deep roots: while at Bletchley Park, Welchman had seen that much of the German success early in the war owed to innovative use of radio communications. The concept of *blitzkrieg* (rapid, disruptive penetration of enemy lines, often achieved by racing around entrenched defenses), for example, depended on interlocking, common-user radio nets that enabled *Panzer* (tank) division commanders to coordinate activity around them, call in air strikes when needed, and maintain constant contact with headquarters. The result was "speed of attack through speed of communications" and a revolution in battlefield tactics.[68]

What the Germans knew and Welchman and his British colleagues had discovered remained largely unknown for decades due to "over-prolonged secrecy imposed on anything to do" with Bletchley Park. During the postwar years, Welchman wrote, "the planning of battlefield communications gradually deteriorated into little more than methods of applying telephone-system thinking and switchboard technology to provide a rigid structure of point-to-point communications."[69] That mode of operation, Welchman believed, was long-since obsolete in light of what modern communications technology could bring to the battlefield. In particular, he realized that "digital packets" containing short bursts of information and broadcast over high-capacity, common-user radios could provide attackers with a tremendous advantage. By 1968, his ideas had evolved into "a general-purpose battlefield communications system that could handle teletype, digital data, digitized voice, and digitized pictures."[70]

Welchman illustrated the workings of this system with an inverted "U" or horseshoe to represent an "information pipeline" or bus (*see illustration on page 74*).[71] Eventually refined under an architecture known as "time division multiple access" (TDMA), this bus was divided into small, sequential intervals called time slots.[72] Aircraft, and conceivably ground or naval forces, would be assigned a discrete time slot in which to feed position and status information in digital packets. This information would be updated at precisely defined intervals in a continuous cycle—a characteristic that led Welchman to describe the entire system as a "cyclic information system."[73]

Later, Welchman chose to highlight another aspect of the problem of battlefield communications—and another benefit of his proposed system. His studies of military engagements across a wide sweep of history reaffirmed a problem labeled by the Prussian military strategist Clausewitz as "the fog of war" (challenges of limited information and rationality in combat situations). MITRE's Eric Ellingson recast this problem as a series of crisply stated propositions that described communications failures on the battlefield:

- people who have information don't know who needs it;

- people who need information don't know who has it; and

- there is no directory to enable the two populations to find each other.[74]

The proposed digital radio system appeared to rectify these problems. Because it relied on broadcast communications rather than point-to-point connections, up-to-date information would be available to all subscribers at all times. The abundant number of transmitters and receivers would enable the network to withstand the loss of particular point sources. And subscribers could decide what information to retrieve. A pilot, for example, could choose to listen selectively for information pertinent to the immediate situation of the aircraft, as opposed to irrelevant data pouring in from other areas. Welchman labeled this concept, "selective access to information," or SATI.[75]

Welchman's work on battlefield information systems coincided with MITRE's work on a transportable, long-range navigation system called Loran-D that was designed for tactical operations in Vietnam. In 1970, the Air Force agreed to fund a small-scale demonstration project of a position location reporting

70. *Ibid.*, 263.

71. *Ibid.*, 264. The version of the horseshoe used here is drawn from "PLRACTA: A New Approach to Tactical Communications," *MITRE Matrix,* vol. 3, no. 5 (September-October 1970), 12.

72. U.S. Air Force Electronic Systems Command, *Introduction to Joint Tactical Information Distribution System (JTIDS),* February 2, 1994, 5.

73. W. G. Welchman, "Concept of Cyclic Information Systems for the Handling of Tactical Information," MITRE Technical Report 701 V2 (1968).

74. Ellingson interview, September 29, 1997.

75. W. G. Welchman, "Selective Access to Tactical Information (SATI): A Brief Introduction," MITRE Working Paper WP 3165, 1970.

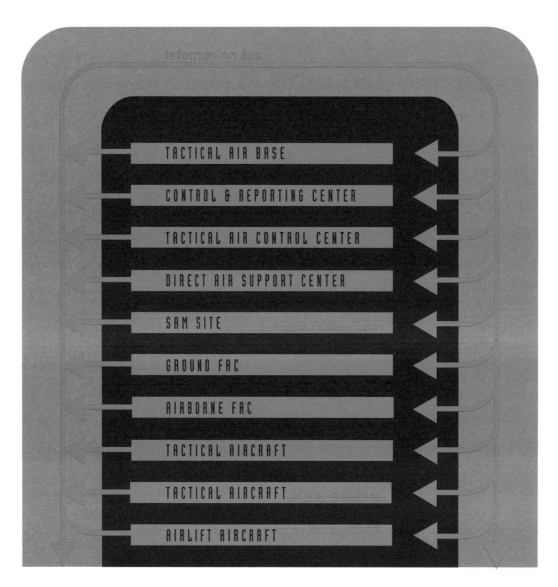

Welchman used an inverted "U" chart to illustrate the cyclic information concept later embodied in JTIDS. Each source point broadcast and continuously updated pertinent information that others could tap selectively, depending upon their situation and needs.

system derived from Loran-D and also incorporating some of Welchman's ideas. The demonstration system was known as Position Location, Reporting and Control of Tactical Aircraft—a designation chosen because the Air Force general officer in charge hated acronyms and wanted a name that would be unpronounceable. (That hope was quickly dashed, and the program was known as PLRACTA— pronounced "pluh-rak-tuh").

To demonstrate PLRACTA, MITRE assembled a resourceful team of engineers that included project manager Ellingson, 33-year-old Victor DeMarines, a future president and CEO of MITRE, and Don Neuman, a future vice president of MITRE. The team cobbled together a system of six terminals—three on the ground, two aboard aircraft, and one mounted on a truck—from off-the-shelf components and used equipment. The transceivers were modified 1950-vintage equipment; the truck that carried the mobile ground unit hailed from the same era; and the computers were surplus machines from the dwindling F-111 program. The equipment and associated software was designed to test the TDMA architecture as well as recursive position-finding and clock synchronization computations, and the fact that it was done "on the cheap" was important to champions of the system. As DeMarines said, "We intend to test PLRACTA's viability in a reasonably short time, with as little newly designed equipment as possible. If there are problem areas, we want to find them before the program is committed to full-capability equipment."[76]

76. "PLRACTA: A New Approach to Tactical Communications," 15.

77. Ellingson interview, October 7, 1997; Victor DeMarines interview, August 12, 1997.

MITRE carried out the "Demonstration 70" of PLRACTA during the winter of 1970-1971. "We would drive the equipment to various places in Boston," Ellingson recalled:

My favorite spot was Prospect Hill in Waltham because there was a solar observatory there. Basically by driving around we determined that we could communicate on the fly at different locations and that we could synchronize the system. We could actually look at a CRT and see the aircraft flying around. In fact I even had a TV monitor on my desk. I remember somebody being in the office and asking about it and I mentioned that we had a flight in the air at the time. I turned on the TV and it had the track going across the TV screen. My visitor asked where the plane was, and I pointed and said, "right here. It'll come flying by in about 15 seconds. Go over to the window and you'll see him fly by." The visitor went over to the window and, sure enough, the aircraft flew by. That was pretty remarkable.[77]

By early 1971, MITRE had demonstrated that PLRACTA was a feasible system. At that point, however, the company discovered that the easy part of the development was over. The system had yet to gain widespread support in the Air Force, where pilots resisted additional electronic equipment in the cockpit and aircraft program managers questioned the expense, size, and weight of the

75 | Case Three: The JTIDS Journey

system in light of its still unproven value. For the system to achieve its maximum utility, moreover, it would need the support of other branches of the service—so that, for example, it could update the status not only of aircraft but also of ground or sea forces. That would require a level of joint cooperation in systems development that would not come readily.

PLRACTA's Progeny

In 1971, Gordon Welchman turned 65 and retired from MITRE. The PLRACTA system continued in development, with low-level funding. At one point, it remained in the budget primarily because a champion in the U.S. Department of Defense promoted one of its capabilities—identification of friendly forces (IFF)—as the basis of a next-generation program. In 1972, PLRACTA became part of a bigger Air Force Program called Seek Bus, which aimed at specifying prototype hardware and software for installation, test, and evaluation of the SATI concept. Although this development work also proved successful, the Air Force still showed no signs of committing to a full-scale acquisition of the system.

Fortunately, at this point in the story, MITRE engineer Jack Shay, program director of the AWACS, intervened. Shay persuaded Brigadier General Kendall Russell, the Air Force officer responsible for AWACS development, to use Seek Bus as the command and control data link for an upcoming AWACS demonstration in Europe. Late in 1972, Gen. Russell approved the plan with the first tests scheduled for early in the new year. "The time to prepare the demonstration was very, very, short," Ellingson later wrote. "I can remember being in the shops in E Building on Christmas Eve, about 6:00 or 6:30…[and] the place was still bustling. The guys were in the shelters, putting stuff together and putting electrical cables in, working hard. It was a good example of the intensity and dedication that people had for the project."[78]

In early 1973, Ellingson and his colleagues took an Air Force plane outfitted with a Seek Bus terminal to Ramstein, Germany, where it was linked into ground systems, including the NATO Air Defense Ground Environment, the 412L Air Weapons Control System, the 407L Tactical Air Control System, and the Hawk surface-to-air missile system. The demonstration was a great success, indicating that Seek Bus had tremendous potential for use in air defense.

Ellingson and his colleagues headed back to the United States to continue work on the Seek Bus terminals, adding anti-jamming and cryptographic security features. The need for such features had been demonstrated in Vietnam, where an adversary with unsophisticated technology was able to intercept communications. In 1975,

An early version of JTIDS known as Position Location, Reporting, and Control of Tactical Aircraft (PLRACTA) used mobile ground stations to broadcast and receive information.

78. Eric Ellingson, "The European Demonstration: A JTIDS Perspective," in *MITRE and AWACS: A Systems Engineering Perspective* (Bedford, Massachusetts: The MITRE Corporation, 1990), 46.

the MITRE team returned to Europe for another demonstration, this time in the United Kingdom. The system was installed on a Navy ship in the Mediterranean and was linked to a U.K. airborne relay operating over the English Channel at 30,000 feet. By this time, virtually all of the technology was in place—the architecture, signal structure, spread spectrum, and security concept—all of which MITRE designed and built in a very short time frame. This demonstration was also successful, and the British were so impressed that they immediately signed up to acquire the system.

The Genesis of JTIDS

NATO forces were not the only ones to appreciate the potential of Seek Bus technology. In 1974, Secretary of Defense James Schlesinger expanded the program for use by all branches of the military, merging Seek Bus with a related U.S. Navy program to form the Joint Tactical Information Distribution System (JTIDS). DOD formed the Joint Service Program Office to administer the program. All four Services participated, with the Air Force in the lead and MITRE as systems engineer.[79]

Enthusiasm for the joint venture was strong on all sides. As AWACS came into operational use, the Air Force saw that JTIDS could give its tactical air control system the secure, jam-proof communications needed against Soviet capabilities. The Navy also recognized the value of JTIDS: it believed that the E2C Hawkeye (its equivalent of AWACS) would benefit from a JTIDS terminal, which could extend air defense coverage around the carrier battle group, tie together the Navy's air and surface warfare networks, and enhance tactical operations. Although the Army did not have the same operational experience, it believed JTIDS could prove useful in tracking and reporting the position of troops on the battlefield.[80]

During the next few years, with MITRE providing technical support, the Air Force developed the Class 1 JTIDS terminal. Built by the Hughes Aircraft Company and designed for use on AWACS aircraft (now called the E-3), the terminal weighed approximately 600 pounds and filled an entire equipment rack in the aircraft. By 1977, prototype Class 1 terminals were installed on E-3 aircraft and undergoing flight tests. The following year, MITRE developed a concept for pod-mounted terminals. The pods made it possible for JTIDS to be installed in fighters without requiring significant modification of the aircraft.[81] MITRE also conceived the Adaptable Surface Interface Terminal (ASIT), which, like the pod, allowed existing Tactical Air Control System elements to interface with JTIDS-equipped aircraft without modification of the elements.[82]

79. C. Kenneth Allard, *Command, Control and the Common Defense* (New Haven: Yale University Press, 1990), 208.

80. Ibid., 213-214.

81. MITRE Corporation, *MITRE: The First Twenty Years*, 228.

82. MITRE Corporation, Operations Highlights, April 1982, 5.

Eric Ellingson led development of PLRACTA and its successors Seek Bus and JTIDS.

As a result of these and other MITRE-initiated refinements, the Class 1 terminal proved a technological success. Production began on schedule in 1983, and by the mid-1980s, JTIDS terminals were implemented in several command-and-control facilities and platforms: the U.S. Air Force Tactical Air Control System elements and E-3s, and U.S. Army air defense system elements. In addition, terminals were added to the NATO E-3A (AWACS) and the NATO air defense ground environments, with hardware and software upgrades added to the NATO ground sites.[83]

Although the Air Force JTIDS effort had managed a strong start, dissension soon developed among the armed services on various aspects of the overall program, including the message standards for implementing JTIDS and, even more important, the system's baseline technological architecture. While the Air Force favored TDMA, a configuration whereby multiple users would be linked to a single common structure (an "internet in the sky," to use today's terms), the Navy had, a decade before the inception of JTIDS, developed an alternative, more decentralized architecture known as Distributed Time Division Multiple Access (DTDMA).[84] The differences between the two architectures were profound and reflected fundamentally different operational environments and needs of the two services.

The Air Force and the Navy also differed in their support for their respective programs. The Navy was a strong proponent of JTIDS, having relied upon digital exchange of data between their ships and aircraft for some time. Ironically, the Air Force was less enthusiastic about the technology it had sponsored. Although the benefits of JTIDS were apparent in the operating of a large AWACS, which could accommodate hefty terminals and equipment, the system was far too large for use in an F-15 fighter. Second, many thought it could overload pilots with information, impeding rather than helping them. Third, JTIDS did not have stand-alone capability but had to be integrated into other systems aboard an aircraft. This problem threatened to become extremely costly, especially if, as in the case of the F-15, the system was not included in the aircraft's original design but had to be installed later. But perhaps most important, proof was still lacking that JTIDS' operational utility justified its expense.[85]

The Class 2 Terminal: the Air Force-Navy Game

The differences between the Air Force and Navy took on increasing importance in the late 1970s, during the planning stages for the next JTIDS generation, the Class 2 terminal. Committed to the need for interoperability and to the joint development of command and control systems, in 1978 the DOD decided that the current version of TDMA (Advanced TDMA, or ATDMA) would be the baseline

A future MITRE vice president, Don Neuman worked closely with Ellingson and future MITRE president Vic DeMarines on JTIDS.

83. MITRE Corporation, Operations Highlights, May 1984, 6.

84. MITRE Corporation, Operations Highlights, September 1982, 6; Allard, *Command Control and the Common Defense*, 216-217.

85. Darrell Trasko, interview, October 21, 1997; Stuart Starr, interview, December 2, 1997.

architecture of JTIDS. When the Navy protested, however, the DOD relented, allowing the Navy to continue developing its own Class 2 DTDMA terminals, provided that they be made interoperable with ATDMA. In allowing two development programs to be carried on simultaneously, this decision widened the growing schism between the Air Force and Navy versions of the system and impeded its development for years.[86]

In January 1981, the Air Force received a go-ahead for full-scale development of the JTIDS Class 2 TDMA terminals for fighter aircraft, including options for its use on the F-15 and F-16. The Air Force awarded a contract for $49.7 million to Singer Kearfott/Rockwell Collins for design, development, and fabrication of 20 terminals for test and evaluation. Built by the General Electric Company (GEC)-Marconi Electronic Systems Corporation and by the Rockwell International Corporation-Collins Avionics and Communications Division (CACD), the Class 2 terminal was far more compact and lighter, measuring 1.6 cubic feet and weighing 125 pounds. With more advanced features than its predecessor, it was designed for small platform JTIDS users, principally fighter aircraft and mobile ground units. MITRE prepared the technical specifications, consulted on source selection, and served as systems engineer.[87]

Meanwhile, the Navy awarded a contract for full-scale development of the DTDMA terminal.[88] DTDMA's ambitious technology, however, proved difficult to implement. Repeated delays and cost overruns led in 1984 to cancellation of the development contract. The House Armed Services Committee hearings that followed voiced the question on every lawmaker's mind: why were two JTIDS architectures necessary? Soon thereafter, the Navy abandoned the DTDMA program and joined the Air Force and Army development efforts.[89]

In this new phase, MITRE began providing support to Navy JTIDS development, in-plant testing, and field test planning of the terminals, efforts that would contribute toward a program milestone, the successful flight of a JTIDS terminal aboard a Navy E-2C Hawkeye surveillance aircraft in 1990. MITRE also oversaw the integration of terminals into all of the Navy's JTIDS platforms: carriers, cruisers, destroyers, and F-14Ds.[90]

Free from the controversy that had embroiled its sister service organizations, the Army, with system engineering support from MITRE, adapted the TDMA technology for its own use. The Class 2M terminal, a down-sized variant of the Class 2 terminal, would eventually be used for tactical command and control.[91]

86. Allard, *Command Control and the Common Defense*, 220-222. For interservice rivalry in weapon systems development, see Merton Peck and Frederick Scherer, *The Weapons Acquisition Process* (Boston: Harvard Business School Press, 1962).

87. MITRE Corporation, Operations Highlights, September 1981, 8–9.

88. MITRE Corporation, Operations Highlights, September 1982, 5.

89. Allard, *Command Control and the Common Defense*, 232–234.

90. MITRE Corporation, Operations Highlights, May 1990, 10.

91. MITRE Corporation, Operations Highlights, February 1983, 6; Allard, *Command Control and the Common Defense*, 235.

At the same time, MITRE continued to provide support for the upgrading of the Class 2 terminal. Through the JTIDS Class 2 Terminal Product Improvement Program (PIP), during the late 1980s and early 1990s, MITRE staff developed ideas for terminal refinements—new hardware and software—designed to reduce unit costs and improve reliability. [92]

Meanwhile, the JTIDS Class 2 terminal began acquiring a larger international following, with implementation aboard British and French E-3s, fighter aircraft, and ships and integration with NATO tactical systems. The performance of JTIDS during the 1990-1991 crisis in the Persian Gulf greatly increased its visibility. Still in the planning stages at the time of the Iraqi attack on Kuwait, the Joint Surveillance Target Attack Radar System (Joint STARS) aircraft could view enemy ground forces while flying over friendly territory, but had no way of detecting or receiving warning of enemy aircraft that might be flying in friendly territory, or of possible collisions with friendly aircraft. The MITRE-developed prototype JTIDS Information Display System (JIDS) remedied this problem. It also facilitated communication between Joint STARS and AWACS aircraft, and helped in the hunt for Iraqi Scud launchers.[93]

Despite these successes, some Air Force leaders continued to harbor reservations about using JTIDS in fighter aircraft. Installation cost at least $500,000 per plane, and this figure did not include development costs. That perspective changed dramatically in June 1993, when, in response to a congressional directive, the Air Force equipped a squadron of F-15s with Class 2 terminals at the Mountain Home Air Base in Idaho. In an exercise with "aggressor planes"—F-5s trained in Russian tactics—the F-15s, with the new situational awareness made possible by JTIDS, easily defeated their opponents. After that, the Air Force needed no further convincing of the value of the system. [94]

JTIDS: The Next Generation

Even as the Class 2 terminals went into production, MITRE was looking ahead to the next wave of JTIDS technology. In the mid-1980s, MITRE had begun work on the Very High Speed Integrated Circuit (VHSIC), advanced electronics that had the potential to double the speed of instructions to 1.6 million per second. At the same time, the VHSIC technology had the potential to reduce the size of the Class 2 terminal by two-thirds, from 1.6 cubic to 0.5 cubic foot. MITRE provided engineering guidance on technology development, terminal architecture, platform integration, and system interoperability issues.[95]

92. MITRE Corporation, Operations Highlights, May 1993, 9.

93. "Maximizing Information Technologies in Desert Storm," *MITRE Matters*, May 6, 1991

94. MITRE Corporation, Operations Highlights, October 1992, 6; Harold Sorenson interview, October 1, 1997.

95. MITRE Corporation, Operations Highlights, May 28, 1986.

Facing page:

As technology advanced, miniaturization of components enabled JTIDS terminals to be installed in Air Force fighters for a convincing demonstration of the system's effectiveness.

As MITRE had anticipated, the VHSIC proved essential to the development of the next generation of JTIDS, the Multifunctional Information Distribution System (MIDS), or Class 2LV (Low Volume) terminal. Smaller, more reliable, and lighter than the Class 2 terminal and compatible with it, the MIDS terminal could be installed in fighter aircraft with limited space, such as the F-16 and F-18, significantly increasing the number of JTIDS-equipped forces.[96] Realizing the potential of MIDS, four foreign nations joined with the United States to support development of the terminal. Because the new terminal was to be significantly smaller than its Class 2 predecessor, the greatest challenge was to reduce the size of the digital electronics. MITRE engineers supported the DOD in the terminal's definition and development phases.[97]

By the mid-1990s, the JTIDS family consisted of four different terminal types, each designed and developed for specific needs:

- Class 1 Terminal: implemented in large-scale airborne and surface command and control systems.

- Class 2 Terminal: implemented in aircraft and mobile command and control elements.

- Class 2M Terminal: a down-sized variant intended for use in Army ground applications.

- Class 2LV or MIDS: intended for use in space-constrained platforms, including fighter aircraft.[98]

After more than 30 years of evolution, JTIDS is now becoming a fully operational command and control system, providing information distribution, position location, and identification capabilities for the Air Force, Army, Navy, Marine Corps, and British, French, and NATO forces. When conceived in the late 1960s, it was a very elegant system designed for future expansion and adaptation, a significant advance that has stood the test of time. Like other pioneering systems, JTIDS endured setbacks—insufficient funding, organizational, and technological problems—any one of which could have proven fatal to the program. Thanks to the support of its believers—MITRE prominent among them—it survived. In 1994, Emmett Paige, OSD/C3I, mandated JTIDS (also known as Link 16) as the DOD tactical data link designed to support land, sea, and air forces in a fully integrated fashion.

Today JTIDS is the longest continuously running and most widely used command and control system in existence. It has at last won many admirers, especially as part of Link 16. Vice Admiral Arthur K. Cebrowski, director of Space, Information Warfare, Command and Control for the U.S. Navy, observed, "it is perhaps the

96. "JTIDS Overview Description," *MITRE Matters*, February 1993.

97. MITRE Corporation, Operations Highlights, May 1988, 20.

98. "JTIDS Overview Description," 35.

single most important system that we have right now for suppressing friendly fire. It is critically important to our forces."[99]

There is still work to do, however. Although Desert Storm heralded the advances of technology to the general public, military experts took a very different view of the operation: Desert Storm (and subsequent operations in Bosnia and Herzegovina) showed that the success of operations involving multiple coalition and allied forces was limited by systems interoperability. In 1996, the Joint Chiefs of Staff issued Joint Vision 2010, a statement that promotes increasing coordination of activity among branches of the military and between U.S. and allied forces. As this future unfolds, the example and lessons of JTIDS may hasten productive change—and create additional overseas opportunities for MITRE.

99. Vice Admiral Arthur Cebrowski interview, January 7, 1998.

January 7
First two JTIDS terminals
for E-3A are delivered

January 20
Jimmy Carter is inaugurated as
39th President of the United
States

February 15
Seattle, Washington site opens

March 24
First E-3A is delivered

March 1
U.S.-China establish embassies

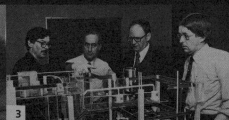

1   In the 1970s, MITRE
engineered the computer
facilities at the heart of
the Worldwide Military
Command and Control
System.

2   The burgeoning work in
civil systems included
"telehealth" and...

3   ...new energy technologies
such as coal liquefaction.

4   During the 1970s MITRE
took on more work for the
U.S. Navy, developing new
systems for secure voice
communications.

July 4
United States observes
bicentennial of Declaration of
Independence

July 7
London, England site opens

August 1
MITRE forms Metrek
Division to manage civilian
government projects

September 20
Frankfurt, Germany site opens

October 15
Stuttgart, Germany site opens

May 1
Neubrucke, Germany site
opens

September 6
Heidelberg, Germany site
opens

September 23
MITRE hires 10,000th
employee

October 1
Venezuela site opens

July 1
Ft. Huachuca, Arizona site
opens

July 21
MITRE's 20th anniversary;
contract revenues exceed $94
million

August
MITRE commences
engineering support for Army
Communications Research
and Development Command
(Ft. Monmouth, NJ)

September 5
San Antonio, Texas site opens

December
NATO approves procurement
of AWACS

1979

January
Defense Intelligence Agency retains MITRE to support Department of Defense Intelligence Information System (DODIIS)

January
Islamic fundamentalists come to power in Iran, setting in motion events leading to another energy crisis

January 8
Camp Smith, Honolulu, Hawaii site opens

February 5
Ft. Monmouth, New Jersey site opens

March 15
Athens, Greece site opens

March 31
Israel and Egypt sign peace accord at Camp David

May 1
Mons, Belgium site opens

May 8
MITRE holds local area network symposium in Boston

July 25
Omaha, Nebraska site opens

August 1
Brunssum, Netherlands site opens

November 4
Iranian militants seize U.S. Embassy in Teheran

1980

April 21
DEC PDP-11/70 computer is installed at Bedford

June 2
San Diego, California site opens

August 28
Video disc technology laboratory is established in Washington

1981

IBM introduces personal computer (8088) with MS/DOS 1.0

January 20
Ronald Reagan is inaugurated as 40th President of the United States

4

May 18
MITRE installs first multifunctional terminal on MITRENET

August 3
Professional Air Traffic Controllers Organization (PATCO) goes on strike

September
Metrek is awarded first patent for spread spectrum method and apparatus

September 1
Munich, Germany site opens

September 1
Norfolk, Va. site opens

September 14
Madrid site opens

October 13
MITRE hosts first National Security Issues Symposium in Bedford

1982

The term "Internet" is used for the first time to describe emerging network of computer networks

January 29
First NATO AWACS is delivered

April 23
First meeting of JASON is held at MITRE

October 1
Rome, Italy site opens

December 5
On-line recruiting begins at MITRE

January
SACDIN passes second initial operational test and evaluation

January
Space Shuttle carries MITRE/WPI experiments

Securities and Exchange Commission requests MITRE assistance in developing pilot program for the electronic collection and dissemination of information

MITRE begins engineering support to joint use FAA/U.S. Air Force Radar Replacement Program

February
Army intelligence analysts begin experiments utilizing MITRE-developed artificial intelligence program

January 21
Joint ESD/MITRE Berlin Air Traffic Control Radar System becomes operational

IBM develops a one-million bit RAM

January 26
Strategic Air Command Intelligence Data Handling System becomes fully implemented, capping seven-year effort

March 23
President Reagan announces Strategic Defense Initiative (SDI) or "Star Wars" program

March
Two MITRE Staff named American Representatives to NATO Air Command and Control Study Team

October 25
U.S. and Caribbean forces liberate Grenada

October 25
National Security Issues Symposium held at MITRE

5

5   Pave Paws, an Air Force program of the 1970s and early 1980s, used state-of-the-art radar systems to warn of incoming missile threats.

6   MITRE hosted symposia on important topics, including this 1981 gathering of experts on national security.

November
AWACS is delivered to Saudi Arabia

7   By the mid-1980s, Bedford Operations had evolved into a sprawling campus of facilities.

8   Meanwhile, Washington Operations spread through a series of office buildings in McLean, Virginia.

An Expanding Role
1976–1986

An Expanding Role, 1976–1986

During the late 1970s and early and mid-1980s, MITRE continued to pursue the general strategy that it had developed in its first decade, with considerable success. Between fiscal years 1976 and 1986, the company's contract revenues rose by a factor of five, from $72.5 million to $363 million, and employment from 2,533 to about 5,200. MITRE experienced rapid growth in every area of its business. For its biggest customer, the Air Force, it supported a host of command, control, and communications (C^3) systems at both strategic and tactical levels. For its non-defense customers, the Metrek Division grew apace, attracting new business in state and local governments. Meanwhile, the biggest new area of opportunity opened up with customers in defense beyond the Air Force. The Reagan defense buildup of the early 1980s boosted the company's work in C^3 systems for all branches of the service, as well as for the intelligence community.

MITRE's work for the Air Force included continuing technical assistance on the AWACS and JTIDS programs. In 1977, the first operational E-3 AWACS aircraft was delivered to the Tactical Air Command, and MITRE continued to support the production of additional AWACS systems, including some bought by U.S. allies in Europe and the Middle East. The E-3s also carried JTIDS terminals, and MITRE developed and upgraded that system for eventual use by all branches of the service. (*See Cases 2 and 3.*) Other major Air Force programs of the era included continuing support, enhancements, and upgrades to long-standing programs such as:

■ The North American Air Defense (NORAD) command and control systems complex at Cheyenne Mountain, near Colorado Springs;

■ Strategic Air Command (SAC) command and control systems, including systems engineering for the SAC Digital Information Network (SACDIN) and the SAC Automated Total Information Network (SATIN-IV);

■ Development of the E-4B Advanced Airborne Command Post, a highly modified Boeing 747 for use by the President and other national command authorities as a mobile command and control center; and

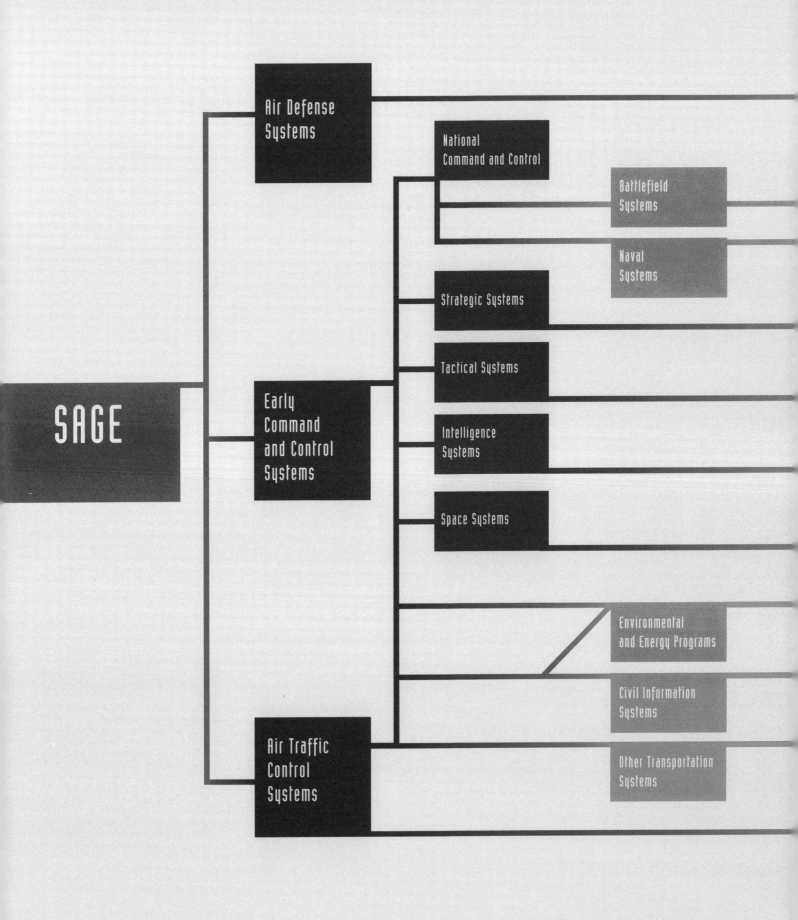

SAGE

Air Defense
Systems

Early
Command
and Control
Systems

Air Traffic
Control
Systems

National
Command and Control

Battlefield
Systems

Naval
Systems

Strategic Systems

Tactical Systems

Intelligence
Systems

Space Systems

Environmental
and Energy Programs

Civil Information
Systems

Other Transportation
Systems

The Metrek Division headed by Herbert Benington managed MITRE's work in civil systems. The division included many personnel recruited from nontraditional backgrounds, including psychology Ph.D Lydia Thomas (top).

100. Lydia Thomas interview, November 4, 1997; Richard S. Greeley, Not-for-Profit: My Non-Military Career at MITRE (Well Off the Beaten Track) (unpublished manuscript, March 10, 1998).

- A succession of ballistic missile early warning programs featuring phased-array radar systems (including sensors, data links, computers, and displays) to detect launches from land or sea.

MITRE also developed or helped develop systems in new areas or incorporating new technologies. Among these initiatives were:

- Support to the Air Force Space Systems Command, including work on the Air Force Satellite Communications program and planning for its successor, the Milstar satellite communication system. MITRE's contributions particularly involved secure, survivable, and jam-resistant communications;

- Have Quick and Seek Talk, programs in multiple generations to develop secure, anti-jam radio ground-to-air voice radio communications;

- Operational Application of Special Intelligence Systems (OASIS—*see Case 4*), a tactical system for gathering and distributing battlefield intelligence, including an intelligence "fusion" center in Germany.

At the Washington-based Metrek Division, where Herbert Benington and S. William Gouse served as successive general managers, business flourished as many civilian departments and agencies came to value MITRE's technical expertise, systems perspective, and objectivity just as much as did the Air Force. Many of these departments and agencies were beginning to understand how new information systems could make their operations more efficient and reliable, and they appreciated MITRE's help. For their part, Metrek personnel took pride in providing a high level of public service and supporting high-priority public initiatives. "We used to track ourselves against Presidential initiatives," recalls Lydia W. Thomas, a psychology Ph.D who joined MITRE in the early 1970s and rose to senior management in Metrek the following decade. "Certain programs, both military and civilian, would be featured in the State of the Union address. Invariably, we would have a hit rate of involvement on these between 75 and 95 percent."[100]

Metrek also helped to define and shape public policy initiatives—and attract attention—by hosting symposia or commissioning study committees on emerging topics and then publishing the proceedings. During the late 1970s, for example, the division sponsored symposia or studies on climate change, policy evaluation, Social Security, alternative energy sources, and women in science. Its major civil systems activities, however, occurred in areas related to air traffic control, the environment, energy, space, and information systems.[101] Representative programs and projects from the era included:

- For the Federal Aviation Administration, MITRE supported the implementation of the National Airspace System (NAS) in the 1970s and helped with enhancements and improvements, especially in collision warning systems, automated decision-support tools for air traffic control, and traffic flow monitoring. In the 1980s, MITRE assisted the FAA and its industrial contractors with a long-term program to modernize the NAS. (*See Case 6.*)

- For the Environmental Protection Agency, MITRE provided support in compiling and analyzing data needed to support regulatory approaches to managing hazardous waste and environmental cleanup. MITRE also carried out many analytical studies of environmental issues, including evaluation of pilot technology for recycling resources.

- For the Department of Energy, MITRE carried out many studies, analyses, and evaluations of new and alternative energy technologies, including coal liquefaction and gasification, solar energy, fuel cells, and geothermal energy.

- For the National Aeronautics and Space Administration, MITRE continued to provide acquisition support and analysis of computer systems for mission control, simulation, training, and administrative applications at the Johnson Space Flight Center in Houston. MITRE also supported the major NASA programs of the period, including systems for the Space Shuttle, Space Station, and Tracking and Data Relay Satellite System.

- For government agencies including the Post Office, the General Services Administration, the Social Security Administration, and the Internal Revenue Service, MITRE provided systems engineering and acquisitions support for new computer and telecommunications systems, local area networks, and automation of record-keeping and other administrative functions.

101. Many of MITRE's ventures in civil systems are summarized briefly in MITRE Corporation, *The MITRE Corporation: Challenge and Response, 1958-1988* (Bedford, Mass.: The MITRE Corporation, 1989), 26–35.

William Gouse worked closely with Benington and later succeeded him as leader of MITRE's work in civil systems.

During the late 1970s and early 1980s MITRE also attracted a growing volume of work with defense customers outside of the Air Force. Many of the new projects and programs reflected a new DOD emphasis on centralized development of C³ systems that would be interoperable across the respective military services. In 1977, the Carter administration, with congressional encouragement, created a new office in DOD: the Assistant Secretary of Defense for Command, Control, Communications, and Intelligence. The Air Force and MITRE were well positioned to provide leadership in joint-service C³ efforts. In the mid-1970s, the Air Force (especially ESD, with MITRE's support) had responsibility for developing and acquiring 70 percent of the DOD's C³ systems and for maintaining 60 percent of them.[102] MITRE responded to the new DOD emphasis in November 1978 by grouping all of its military C³ activities in a new operating unit called the C³ Division, with Kenneth McVicar as vice president and general manager. This unit, in turn, consisted of two components: Bedford Operations, which supported the Air Force, principally the Electronic Systems Division; and Washington C³ Operations, which worked for the DCA, Army, Navy, and other offices in DOD and the intelligence community.

In addition to JTIDS, the major joint C³ initiatives of the period were the Joint Tactical Communications Program (TRI-TAC), an effort to coordinate planning for digital communications systems and specify common equipment for use in tactical settings; and Tactical Air Control Systems/Tactical Air Defense Systems (TACS/TADS), an effort to achieve interoperability among tactical C³ systems that had been developed separately by the Air Force, Army, Navy, and Marine Corps. Inevitably, these programs were fraught with both technical and organizational difficulties as the services struggled to agree on standards and protocols while viewing the prospect of interbranch cooperation with ambivalence. Nonetheless, TRI-TAC and TACS/TADS—along with JTIDS—led to successful demonstrations that brought MITRE into contact with computer and communications specialists in every branch of the military and increased the company's visibility throughout the DOD.[103]

102. C. Kenneth Allard, *Command, Control, and the Common Defense* (New Haven: Yale University Press, 1990), 194; MITRE Corporation, Annual Report for 1976.

103. MITRE Corporation, *MITRE: The First Twenty Years* (Bedford, Mass.: The MITRE Corporation, 1979), 220 and 242-243; Allard, *Command, Control, and the Common Defense*, 199-200.

Facing page:

In the 1980s MITRE performed a growing volume of work for the U.S. Navy, assisting in the development of command, control, and communications systems. These projects included extremely low frequency communications systems used to communicate with submarines.

In the mid-1970s, the Army Materiel Command engaged MITRE to help develop new battlefield systems—an assignment that led to a burgeoning relationship. In 1979, in support of the Communications-Electronics Command, MITRE established a site at the command's headquarters in Ft. Monmouth, New Jersey. (*See Case 5.*) MITRE's involvement with the intelligence community expanded at the same time. In 1979, the Defense Intelligence Agency, an organization charged to coordinate the intelligence needs of the DOD, the Joint Chiefs of Staff, the unified commands, and their major components, retained MITRE as systems engineer for the Department of Defense Intelligence Information System (DODIIS). This assignment marked the beginning of a major new area of activity for the company in the 1980s and 1990s. (*See Case 4.*)

Meanwhile, the Navy also engaged MITRE to help with its new C³ initiatives. In 1980, the company opened an office in San Diego to support the new Naval Ocean Systems Center in the development and testing of C³ systems for secure, jam-resistant radio communications, submarine communications, electronic countermeasures, target identification, and surveillance. In 1982, MITRE added an office near the Naval Underwater Systems Center in New London, Connecticut, to assist development of extremely low frequency communications systems.[104]

104. MITRE Corporation, *MITRE: The First Twenty Years*,197; MITRE Corporation, Annual Report for 1981.

105. Richard Granato interview, November 4, 1997.

106. Paul Bracken, *The Command and Control of Nuclear Forces* (New Haven: Yale University Press, 1983); Allard, *Command, Control, and the Common Defense,* 135-138; Paul Edwards Paul Edwards, *The Closed World: Computers and the Politics of Discourse in Cold War America* (Cambridge, Mass.: MIT Press, 1997).

107. *MITRE: The First Twenty Years,* 177-181.

At the level of strategic C[3] systems, MITRE's support of the World Wide Military Command and Control System (WWMCCS) led to significantly bigger exposure for the company throughout the Department of Defense.[105] This program, like the National Military Command System (NMCS—*see Interlude 1*), emerged following the Cuban missile crisis, when the President's ability to command and control America's nuclear arsenal became a major strategic priority.[106] Development of NMCS had emphasized ability to survive a nuclear attack. Development of WWMCCS emphasized not only survivability but also flexibility, compatibility, standardization, and economy. By then it was apparent that each branch of the military was designing and building its own information systems that typically featured unique or customized hardware and software. Top officials inside DOD recognized an emerging problem and pushed to develop standards that would ensure basic compatibility while giving priority to a centralized system to support the President as Commander-in-Chief and the unified commands over the particular interests of the specified commands.

In the early 1970s, DOD set as a goal the design and implementation of a WWMCCS to meet the command and control needs of 1985, and IBM was retained as systems architect. During the next several years, the basic outlines of WWMCCS took shape: 27 command centers around the world, each featuring a mainframe computer and common software, with plans to link them through a dedicated communications network. In 1975, the WWMCCS Systems Engineering Organization (WSEO) was created within the Defense Communications Agency, where MITRE provided systems engineering support. WSEO took responsibility for developing system specifications and requirements, including a transition plan that would phase in new capabilities over time. MITRE was retained to help WSEO in this work, while also continuing to support DCA in certain time-critical or technically high-risk tasks within WWMCCS. The company, for example, helped develop the Advanced Airborne Command Post, the Minimum Essential Emergency Communications Network, and other subsystems and components of the overall WWMCCS system. MITRE was also involved in many related activities, including the development of the Prototype WWMCCS Intercomputer Network (PWIN), an initiative to connect computers in the system into a network patterned on the Defense Advanced Research Projects Agency's ARPANET—the forerunner of the Internet. [107]

MITRE's work on strategic C[3] systems accelerated in the early 1980s, when the Reagan administration made modernization of the national command structure a top defense priority. The administration invested more than $18 billion in improvements in connectivity and survivability of the information systems supporting its air, land, and sea forces. These funds supported upgrades and improvements to virtually every C³ system in existence. They also helped to fund major new C³ initiatives such as the Joint Surveillance and Target Attack Radar System (Joint STARS), an airborne system akin to AWACS but designed to detect ground targets at ranges of several hundred miles. [108]

In 1983, President Reagan announced another multibillion dollar defense program, the Strategic Defense Initiative (SDI). Also known as "Star Wars" for the futuristic nature of its technology, SDI imagined a network of satellites and space-based lasers that would detect ballistic missile launches and destroy the missiles during their trajectory through space. The success of SDI required highly sophisticated sensors, computers, communications, and other advanced technologies. In support of SDI, MITRE established a technical evaluation facility to investigate and define C³ architectures and simulate key processes and force interactions.

By the mid-1980s, MITRE was supporting hundreds of programs and projects for defense and civilian government customers. The company continued to push the frontiers of information technology while acquiring important new capabilities and accumulating a wide and deep base of knowledge about its customers and their operational environments and requirements. At the same time, MITRE developed new and valuable expertise in working across organizational boundaries on jointly sponsored programs. These new capabilities would serve MITRE well in following years.

108. Allard, *Command, Control, and the Common Defense,* 191; Bruce G. Blair, *Strategic Command and Control: Redefining the Nuclear Threat* (Washington, D.C.: The Brookings Institution, 1985), 182-280.

Case Four   The Intelink Innovation

During most of the post-World War II era, each member organization in the U.S. intelligence community gathered, analyzed, and disseminated intelligence information according to its own mission and priorities. The result was a wealth of intelligence information and analysis, but much of it was compartmentalized and not readily accessible across the community as a whole. In the early 1990s, the rapid growth of computer networks such as the Internet raised the possibility that vital intelligence information could be pooled and shared.

In 1993, MITRE began working with a high-level group representing the constituents of the intelligence community to implement a new information capability called Intelink. Based on the emerging architecture of the World Wide Web and hosted on the MITRE-developed Joint Worldwide Intelligence Communications System (JWICS) platform, Intelink provides users throughout the community with secure access to intelligence information they are cleared to see, regardless of its point of origin.

Intelink proceeded from idea to prototype in less than six months, testimony to MITRE's intimate knowledge of the fast-evolving world of commercial information technology and its ability to work across the boundaries between government agencies and organizations.

Pictured on overleaf: Intelink overcomes barriers of time, space, and organization, connecting intelligence users in the field with intelligence sources around the world in real time.

The Intelink Innovation

Many of MITRE's assignments during the late 1980s and early 1990s stretched the company to develop new skills and capabilities. The pace of change in information technology was extraordinarily rapid as hardware grew faster and more capable, software more sophisticated yet easier to use, and networks formed and proliferated. In the commercial world, this technology moved out of back offices and specialized departments into everyday operations, changing the way companies organized and competed. Old hierarchies and structures broke down, as did the traditional boundaries between companies and their suppliers, customers, and competitors.

109. Jessica Matthews, "Power Shift," *Foreign Affairs* (January-February 1997), 52.

Whether information technology would exert its transformative power on government operations seemed an open question in the 1990s. One expert, writing in *Foreign Affairs*, noted the potential of this technology to disrupt hierarchies but expressed skepticism about the impact on government:

In a network, individuals or groups link for joint action without building physical or formal institutional presence. Networks have no person at the top and no center. Instead, they have multiple nodes where collections of individuals or groups interact for different purposes. Businesses, citizens organizations, ethnic groups, and crime cartels have all readily adopted the network model. Governments, on the other hand, are quintessential hierarchies, wedded to an organizational form incompatible with all that the new technologies make possible.[109]

At MITRE, executives and engineers took an opposite view, as they saw first hand the effects of new technology on traditional government operations. One of the most dramatic examples occurred in its work for the U.S. intelligence community, where an information technology project of modest scale produced revolutionary changes in the way the community operated. The company's ability to facilitate such change reflected its long history with the customer, its growing expertise in commercial information technology, and its expanding understanding of the organizational implications of its work.

Entering a Dark World

In the aftermath of the successful European AWACS demonstration, MITRE found itself drawn into many new lines of work. One of the most promising was developing systems to gather and distribute intelligence information. Although the company could claim to be in the business of such systems from the

110. The MITRE Corporation,
MITRE: The First Twenty Years.
(Bedford, Mass.: The MITRE
Corporation, 1979), 223.

111. The MITRE Corporation,
MITRE: The First Twenty Years,
223-224.

beginning—SAGE, after all, was arguably a kind of intelligence system—MITRE did not undertake a true intelligence assignment until 1963, when it undertook Project East Wing for the Air Force. This decades-long project entailed analyzing Soviet air defense systems and networks to identify points of vulnerability.

In the mid-1970s, the scale and scope of MITRE's work for the intelligence community began to grow significantly. In April 1973, the Air Force asked MITRE "to consider ways in which special intelligence data might help [AWACS] give warning against potential threats." At the same time, General David C. Jones, the commander of the Air Forces in Europe, and Major General W. L. Creech, his deputy chief of staff for operations and intelligence, urged the establishment of a U.S.-owned facility in the central region of NATO to provide intelligence for all Air Force tactical operations in the region.[110]

When General Creech assumed command of the Electronic Systems Division at Hanscom Air Force Base the following year, he authorized the start of the Operational Application of Special Intelligence Systems (OASIS) program, with MITRE as systems engineer. OASIS was designed to obtain timely and relevant intelligence data from a variety of sources, including Project East Wing, and make it accessible and useful to tactical air commanders. By then, MITRE was well equipped to take on this role because of its knowledge of enemy air operations and growing capabilities in communications, computer security, and information management.

Technician Margaret Calder operates an interactive display terminal for the Operational Application of Special Intelligence Systems (OASIS) program in the 1970s.

MITRE's work on OASIS, like all of its major assignments, started with system definition and requirements identification and analysis and proceeded to testing, evaluation, and supervision of continuing refinements. By 1978, MITRE had helped to engineer a "tactical fusion center" in Germany that gathered information from U.S. intelligence sources and funneled it to a NATO air operations command. This information provided U.S. and NATO commanders with much more comprehensive data on Warsaw Pact air operations, which in turn increased protection and safety for friendly military aircraft flying near East-West borders.[111]

Subsequently, MITRE also brought another new and intriguing capability, also originating in JTIDS, to its work for the intelligence community: its growing expertise in information network architecture and distributed processing. In the early 1970s, the company applied time-division, multiple-access (TDMA) architectural principles demonstrated in JTIDS to wideband digital communications over coaxial cable. The result was a patented, cable-based system called MITRIX, and it enabled one of the first local area networks.[112] MITRIX eliminated the need for pairs of wires and point-to-point connections to link computers and other digital devices in fast two-way communications. Data transmission through modems of the era trickled at a speed of 75 baud; MITRIX, in contrast, offered much greater capacity, and it could carry digitized images as well as computer text and data files. The benefit of the new technology was not only speed but compatibility with different types of digital equipment: a terminal with a MITRIX connection could be attached anywhere on the network and could "talk" to any other MITRIX-equipped devices.

At first, applications of MITRIX were simple, enabling different computers to share printers, or facilitating the work of small teams around common files and databases. Once the feasibility of MITRIX was established, applications began to explode: it became the underpinning of MICOM, the state-of-the-art internal network within MITRE that circulated video, audio, and digital information around the company. MITRE developed related technologies and systems to tie together information sources at Air Force bases and other military establishments. It installed experimental cable-based communications systems in hospitals and government agencies, including some in the intelligence community, where broadband capabilities proved important for transmitting and processing of images. Although coaxial cable as a medium and the MITRE-developed protocols eventually gave way to more cost-effective alternatives (especially Ethernet, developed at Xerox's Palo Alto Research Center), the MITRIX experience opened new vistas for MITRE in high-speed digital communications networks.[113] (In the 1990s, digital transmission over coaxial cable re-emerged as a burgeoning business for internet access from private residences.)

The MITRIX experience immediately bore fruit in the company's next major program in the world of intelligence: the Department of Defense Intelligence Information System (DODIIS).[114] This system was the responsibility of the Defense Intelligence Agency (DIA), an organization charged to coordinate the intelligence needs of the DOD, the Joint Chiefs of Staff, the Unified Commands, and their major components. In the late 1970s, leadership at DIA—prodded by Congress—was concerned about the proliferation of independent systems for gathering and distributing intelligence information. At the time, inside the DOD alone, more than 50 individual systems based in more than 30 separate locations were engaged in retrieving and processing intelligence messages, storing and retrieving intelligence data, and supporting the preparation of intelligence products in such areas as indications and warning, order of battle, and targeting.[115]

112. "Going Digital: MITRIX," *MITRE Matrix,* Vol.5, No. 6 (December 1972), 38-56.

In the early 1970s, MITRE built and used one of the first local area networks, a coaxial cable-based system called MITRIX. Here Victor DeMarines (l.)—a future president of MITRE—and David Willard demonstrate a prototype MITRIX interface unit.

113. Victor DeMarines interview, August 12, 1997; David Lehman interview, October 21, 1997. For the origins of Ethernet, see Katie Hafner and Matthew Lyon, *Where Wizards Stay Up Late: The Origins of the Internet* (New York: Simon & Schuster, 1996), 237-240.

Interestingly, MITRE inventions in cable-based networking continue to bear fruit in the late 1990s, with the introduction of cable modems for Internet access.

114. Donald Martell and Aaron Lesser interview, October 2, 1997; Aaron Lesser, The DODIIS Experience, Revision One, November 1996, unpublished typescript at MITRE Corporation.

115. MITRE Corporation, Annual Report for 1980.

The inefficiencies of these arrangements were painfully apparent. The biggest problem was system incompatibility, so that one organization could not easily share information with another. Another problem, brought on by the first, was wasteful duplication of effort. Still another challenge was difficulty in obtaining qualified technical personnel in each service and organization to supervise these systems. A final problem concerned the inter-organizational disputes and turf battles that inevitably cropped up around systems interconnection issues.

116. Lesser, "The DODIIS Experience," 2; Lehman interview, October 14, 1997.

117. Martin Faga interview, September 5, 1997.

In 1979, these considerations led the DIA to seek an FFRDC to provide the major commands with technical guidance for their on-site acquisitions of intelligence systems. After reviewing the capabilities of several potential service providers, the Agency selected MITRE for the assignment, in part because of the company's experience and expertise in engineering digital networks. As directed by Chuck Sheehan, MITRE's work on DODIIS led to a mushrooming of personnel engaged in intelligence work, with small groups of technical staff dispersed to dozens of offices and commands around the world. At the same time, MITRE's work on DODIIS significantly broadened the company's exposure to intelligence customers throughout the DOD. It also kept the company abreast of fast-moving developments in commercial information technology. Finally, DODIIS extended MITRE's growing expertise in engineering digital information networks. During the 1980s, MITRE and the DIA developed an array of management tools to coordinate defense intelligence systems development: in-progress reviews; use of standard system components; technical conferences; site leaders' meetings, and, where necessary, "hold firm" policies on basic standards, such as TCP/IP protocols for use on a local area network. At the same time, MITRE continued to make advances in key technologies such as image processing and secure communications.[116]

In January 1985, MITRE hosted a two-day conference on the Department of Defense Intelligence Information System (DODIIS). Participants included R. B. Walker, Associate Director for DODIIS Planning and Management in the Defense Intelligence Agency (2nd from r.) and MITRE staff (l. to r.) Douglas Gage, David Baldauf, Frank Alden, Program Manager Charles Sheehan, and (seated) Thomas Hilinski.

In the early 1980s, the new Reagan administration pushed for and achieved expanded funding for a host of initiatives in defense, national security, and intelligence. By the middle of the decade, MITRE had several hundred technical staff engaged in intelligence-related work, supporting the Air Force, the Department of Defense, and other agencies that comprise the intelligence community. These assignments covered the full range of intelligence work, from data gathering (through devices), to information distribution and coordination, to analysis. MITRE brought a range of technical and engineering skills to these problems, from data acquisition, encryption, transmission, database management, programming, and image processing.[117]

In 1987, MITRE's top management identified intelligence-related work as a major area of interest and asked Vic DeMarines, director of intelligence and electronic warfare systems in Bedford, to lead a strategic review of MITRE's involvements and capabilities, and how these matched evolving government needs. That assignment confirmed intelligence-related activities as a major area of the company's operations and indicated significant potential for growth. In August 1988, DeMarines became vice president in the C3I Group for Air Force Systems and charged to coordinate MITRE's assignments for the intelligence community.[118]

In his new assignment, DeMarines quickly discovered that MITRE could contribute a unique and impartial view of technical issues evolving inside the intelligence community. "We didn't really appreciate until we focused on it that, while a lot of people know about what's going on in the intelligence community, they tend to know about it from one perspective. Because we had people working intelligence systems issues for the Air Force, Army, Navy, DIA, NSA, and other clients, we had a unique perspective. We could then use that perspective and make some things happen which otherwise could not have been done. We have taken on that mantle as an FFRDC and public-spirited company to work across organizational boundaries and achieve economies and efficiencies that benefit the taxpayers." At the same time, DeMarines noted, MITRE's exposure to a wide range of technical and organizational problems and its pioneering record on the frontiers of information technology provided additional benefits to its customers in the intelligence community.[119]

In 1990, MITRE further emphasized its commitment to intelligence customers by forming the Center for Intelligence and Special Programs (subsequently the Center for Integrated Intelligence Systems [CIIS]), which cut across the previous division between MITRE's Bedford and Washington locations. The new Center expanded the range of services provided by MITRE and embarked on significant new programs. Many of these involved imagery intelligence, tools to support training and decision making, and the definition of security standards for commercially available information technology. MITRE served as systems engineer, for example, on the Joint Service Imagery Processing System (JSIPS). This system was mobile and ruggedized, and it enabled branches of the military to share common imagery—maps, diagrams, reconnaissance and surveillance photographs—in tactical combat situations. MITRE also supported the Special Operations Command Research, Analysis, and Threat Evaluation System (SOCRATES), which played a significant role in providing intelligence support for the U.S. Central Command during the Gulf War.

MITRE made major contributions to computer security in the 1990s by developing new requirements for commercially available information technology

Software engineer John Woodward pioneered key innovations in information security in the 1980s and early 1990s. Today Woodward leads MITRE's work in Information Warfare.

118. DeMarines interview, August 12,1997.

119. DeMarines interview, August 12,1997; Faga interview, September 5, 1997.

and testing them through prototypes. At the DIA's request, MITRE undertook an ambitious project to develop secure workstations running standard UNIX operating systems and X-Windows. Under John Woodward, MITRE established specifications for the Compartmented Mode Workstation, which maintained and kept separate different types of top-secret data. Users of the workstation had access only to information they were cleared to see and were blocked from viewing information that might be available to another user. There were complex rules to enforce this security—for example, prohibiting information to be cut from one window and pasted into another when the user did not have clearance for both.

"The thought that you would merge separate types of information in a system and keep them separate was not a new concept," said Woodward. "The thought of doing it for compartments, as opposed to SECRET versus TOP SECRET was a little bit new, and the idea of tying that separation to Windows was totally new." The Compartmented Mode Workstation proved a major achievement in the management of secure information. "It was really the first time that security was ahead of technology. Usually efforts to secure a system happen about the time the system becomes obsolete. But this was a case in which we showed the value of security in a new technology, windowed workstations, before they became commonplace."[120]

The Intelink Happening

MITRE's mounting expertise in developing intelligence information systems and dealing with interoperability concerns proved invaluable during the early 1990s, when the end of the Cold War and pressures on the federal budget combined to produce steep declines in military spending. In such an environment it became vitally important for the military services and government agencies to work together in information technology development and to find standard solutions. As DOD Secretary William Perry put it in the fall of 1993,

> ...in order to offset our declining resources, we must accelerate the pace at which we define standard baseline processes and data requirements, select and deploy migration systems, implement data standardization, and conduct functional process improvement reviews and assessments (business process re-engineering) within and across all functions of the Department.[121]

As these issues reached the intelligence community, MITRE was well positioned to help. Starting first inside the DOD, DeMarines and other MITRE personnel worked with various intelligence offices to address the incompatibility of their respective systems. In 1993, at MITRE's urging, the Assistant Secretary of Defense for Command, Control, Communications, and Intelligence formed the Intelligence

120. John Woodward interview, November 25, 1997.

121. Quoted in MITRE Corporation, Intelink: An Information Service for Intelligence, (Presentation text and graphics, October 1996), 10.

Systems Council (ISC), which consisted of representatives of the military services and key defense agencies, and which received technical support from MITRE. The ISC attacked the problem of interoperability in two ways: by addressing urgent problems on an ad hoc basis, and by developing a systematic approach to the creation of interoperable technical architectures.

At about the same time, other federal initiatives addressed similar issues. Vice President Gore headed the National Program Review, a major effort to "re-invent" government by bringing state-of-the-art management technologies, including commercially available information systems, into the public sector.

In October, ISC was expanded into a new Intelligence Systems Board (ISB) that was chaired jointly by the Director of Central Intelligence and the Deputy Secretary of Defense, and included representatives of other departments and agencies in the intelligence community. The board was responsible for setting intelligence communication and information system policies and standards;

Chart below:

A high-level, interagency group representing all constituents of the U.S. intelligence community coordinated development of Intelink.

Intelink Stakeholders

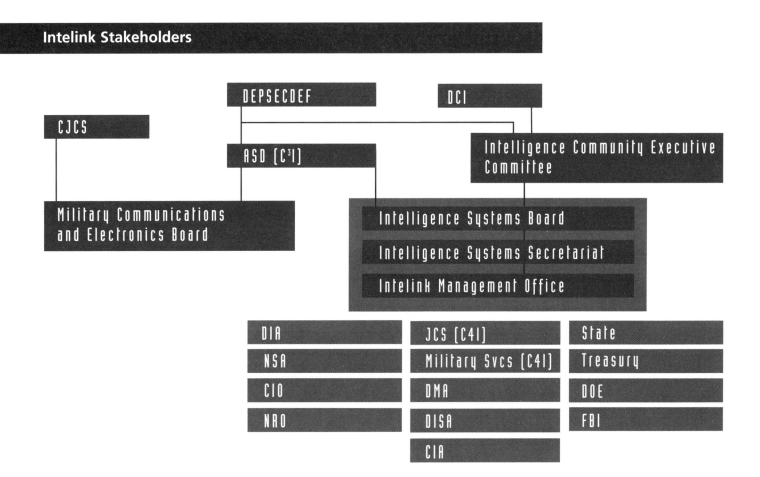

122. Judith A. Furlong, *What Is Intelink?* (MITRE Publication MP 96B0000115, October 1996).

123. Lesser, The DODIIS Experience, 3.

developing top-level information architectures; and establishing organizations, authorities, and procedures to provide central direction of the intelligence community information services and resources.[122] It was supported by the Intelligence Systems Secretariat (ISS), an operating group that was charged to enhance the exchange of information throughout the intelligence community. Steven Schanzer, a senior DIA official, was named as the first ISS director. MITRE, in turn, provided technical support to the ISS.[123]

The members of the ISB and ISS were well aware of the challenges facing them. The central problem was the varying circumstances in which many existing intelligence systems had been developed. Most were stand-alone systems with unique architectures and many customized features—interfaces, standards, security characteristics, hardware, and underlying networks—that inhibited communication with other systems. By their very nature, moreover, these systems had been designed for carefully restricted access with information distributed on a need-to-know basis. As a result, many offices that made use of multiple sources of information required multiple terminals and networks—a costly and inefficient way to work. The more that intelligence community officials examined the problem, the more expensive seemed the solutions. Some estimates ran into the hundreds of millions of dollars to develop a new, secure intelligence information network.

Discussions between Schanzer and DeMarines focused on the imperative to change the way that intelligence information was gathered and disseminated—in short, to change the way the community worked. The challenge, as they saw it, was two-fold. First, there was a need to break down the walls between various agencies, so that intelligence information could more easily be shared, that analysis could occur faster, and that duplication of effort could be minimized. Second, they believed, new information technology could deliver intelligence information into the hands of personnel in the field much more quickly than ever before, with resulting significant benefit to U.S. national security.

Schanzer and DeMarines recognized the potential to meet these needs at a fraction of earlier cost estimates by developing a system similar to emerging commercial information networks such as CompuServe. These networks presented subscribers with a common interface that enabled them through a few simple commands to access a variety of databases and information sources with dissimilar formats. To Schanzer and DeMarines, a similar network that was transparent to the underlying systems and provided users with a consistent look and feel regardless of their location seemed highly desirable for the intelligence community. Schanzer asked MITRE what it might take to set up a CompuServe-like network for the community.

The Intelink development team included Robert Brown, Donald Martell (standing), and Bonnie Blades.

The MITRE team was led by Don Martell, then department head of Defense Intelligence Information Systems. He and his colleagues started by investigating CompuServe and other commercially available systems. But they also recognized that an alternative technology, the World Wide Web, was on the verge of explosive growth and might better serve the intelligence community's needs. Although the Web had been in existence since 1990 as a means of moving from site to site on the Internet through "hyper-links," the catalyst for the Web's booming growth was the availability of the first user-friendly Web navigation tool, or "browser," called Mosaic. Developed at the National Center for Supercomputing Applications (NCSA) at the University of Illinois, Mosaic enabled users to jump from site to site with a simple on-screen "point-and-click" device. Mosaic worked with almost all computing platforms ranging from PCs to super computers and all major operating systems. The initial version of Mosaic was introduced early in 1993, with a Windows-compatible version available in October.[124]

124. Robert H. Reid, *Architects of the Web: 1,000 Days that Built the Future of Business* (New York: John Wiley & Sons, Inc., 1997), xxiii-xxvi and Chapter 1.

125. Martell and Lesser interview, October 2, 1997.

126. Woodward interview, November 25, 1997.

Martell and the MITRE team immediately recognized the potential of a Web-based technology like Mosaic to meet the needs of the intelligence community quickly and cost-effectively, and they arranged an early demonstration for Schanzer and other government officials. "Here was software that could run on any computer in the Department of Defense or the intelligence community," Martell pointed out. "It doesn't matter where you are or what equipment you're using: the interface is the same. And it's easy to navigate and find things."[125]

At the same time, MITRE spotted another opportunity to implement a Web-like system quickly. During the early 1990s, the company had engineered a secure data communications network for the Department of Defense called JWICS—Joint Worldwide Intelligence Communications System. Developed on a crash schedule, JWICS relied on an architecture similar to that of the Internet and it already linked various intelligence offices inside the DOD.[126] By extending JWICS to other members of the intelligence community, adding server and browser software freely available from the NSCA, and designing a new interface, MITRE could rapidly and cost-effectively test an entirely new and extraordinarily powerful intelligence capability: a point-and-click, user-friendly, interoperable, multimedia information service.

Intelink provides users with a point-and-click interface to pertinent intelligence information anywhere on the globe.

In December 1993, the ISS formed an Architecture Panel, a working group charged to develop a top-level architecture for intelligence information exchange and dissemination. This panel authorized MITRE to proceed with an experiment of the Web-like service named Intelink. The goal was a demonstration of the capability on a half-dozen servers by the spring of 1994, with total funding set at approximately $350,000.

127. Woolsey/Deutch memo, August 11, 1994, quoted in MITRE Corporation, Intelligence Information Dissemination: Part of the Problem (Presentation text and graphics to U.S. Senate, 1997), 10.

128. Another version, fielded by the Community Open Source Program Office, was called "Intelink-U" for Unclassified or open source information. It sought to make information from unclassified sources readily available to the community and enable users to share information with one another at the unclassified level. This version operated over private lines and tunneling over the Internet.

Meanwhile, other systems adopted the Intelink architecture model and used the Intelink name although they were not officially condoned. Best known is Intelink-CI, which services eight agencies within the counterintelligence community. Other Intelink variants have been proposed to focus on cooperation with U.S. allies, e.g., Intelink-C for activities with the Commonwealth nations and Intelink-NATO or for activities within NATO nations.

129. Faga interview, September 5, 1997.

130. Martell and Lesser interview, October 2, 1997.

During the next five months, MITRE personnel already in the field supporting DODIIS began to install World Wide Web software on military servers around the world. The ISS persuaded customers in these locations to allow representative content— structured databases, finished intelligence products, imagery, maps, and general reference information—to be accessible via the new system and obtained a waiver to the intelligence community's "need-to-know" principle from the Deputy Director of Central Intelligence. The national intelligence agencies also implemented the capability using their own personnel.

By April 1994, Intelink was up and running on 19 servers with dozens of users around the world. A demonstration to senior officials of the intelligence community proved a resounding success. In August, a memo jointly signed by the Deputy Secretary of Defense and the Director of Central Intelligence designated Intelink as "the *strategic direction* for Community product dissemination systems." At the same time, these officials directed the ISS "to ensure effective integration of INTELINK into classified or unclassified architectures."[127]

During the ensuing months, MITRE worked with the ISS and member organizations to establish a permanent Intelink Service Management Center based at the NSA. MITRE also assisted in making operational three different versions of Intelink:

■ The original system was expanded and became known as Intelink TS-SCI (top secret, secure compartmented information).

■ A parallel system, Intelink-S, functioned at the "secret" security level and used the Defense Information Systems Network rather than JWICS as the underlying network. Intelink-S became operational in December 1994 and was designed to support military operational forces as well as international law enforcement in areas such as counternarcotics and antiterrorism. It was destined to become the primary intelligence medium for the DOD Global Command and Control System.

■ Another version, Intelink-P, for policy makers, was established in the fall of 1995. Access to Intelink-P was restricted to the President and senior officials from the executive and legislative branches. It operated at top security level and used private lines for its network connectivity.[128]

By the late-1990s, the Intelink system was evolving rapidly to expand its content, range, and features, including electronic mail and directory services. At the same time, the nature of the system began to change. Dissemination of intelligence information could occur through both "push" (broadcast) and "pull" (search) arrangements. Intelink also expanded its role beyond intelligence information dissemination, to analytical research support, collaborative development of intelligence products, training, and administrative functions.

Although there was some resistance to implementing Intelink, once the service was demonstrated in a prototype experiment, the skepticism quickly evaporated and the system was declared operational. In the summer of 1996, Intelink TS-SCI had more than 40,000 users and was accessed more than 300,000 times per week. Typical uses included preparation and distribution of daily and special intelligence assessments, summaries of "hot spots" (e.g., Chechnya, North Korea, Iraq), background capability studies, and extensive finished intelligence products. Through electronic publishing, more than 80 percent of the NSA's production was available to members of the community within two hours.

"Once people saw Intelink, they immediately recognized its value," said Marty Faga, senior vice president and general manager of CIIS. Faga pointed out that agencies that were initially reluctant to make their data available on line had sudden changes of heart once they gained experience with Intelink. Instead of hoarding information, users began competing to put more information on line while providing better and better ways to organize and present it. Some agencies had also worried that information would become too easily available and could be distorted if pulled out of the context of, say, a finished analytical report. That concern also proved unfounded, as information available on Intelink manifested an immediacy and complexity sometimes lost in the production of traditional intelligence reports. In short, concluded Faga, "The power of the technology overcame the concerns."[129]

Marty Faga led the Center for Integrated Intelligence Systems between 1995 and 1998, when he became executive vice president and director of the DOD FFRDC.

Intelink became operational as an initiative with extraordinarily high leverage. Developed at a cost of several hundred thousand dollars at a time when CIIS was working on more than $100 million in programs, Intelink generated enormously significant changes in the way the intelligence community worked. In 1995, Vice President Gore recognized the program for a Golden Hammer Award for "helping to substantially change the way government does business." But Intelink also represented a new way for MITRE to work in the 1990s. "I think it's important to point out that when we started there was no budget," Don Martell recalled. "Intelink was not specified anywhere as a project or program of any of the intelligence agencies or the DOD. There was no program office, no plan, no line item. I hesitate even to call it a project because Intelink was more of a happening than anything else."[130]

1986

1987

1988

MITRE study anticipates growth of U.S. intelligence initiatives

March 18
Piedmont Airlines Flight No. 74 becomes the first commercial flight to use TCAS

July
After 17 years as president, Robert Everett retires. Charles Zraket becomes MITRE president

July
MITRE begins work on FTS 2000 (Federal Telephone System)

DCA/MITRE holds planning seminar on "The 21st Century Defense Communications System"

May
Army accepts JTIDS Class 2M terminals

July
Video Teleconferencing Center debuts at Hanscom AFB as part of Strategic Defense Initiative

October 1
James Schlesinger becomes chairman of the MITRE Board of Trustees

October 1
Barry Horowitz appointed executive vice president and chief operating officer

December 9
GSA awards FTS 2000 contract to MITRE

1989

January
Major AWACS Improvement Program commences to extend platform's projected utility by 20 years

January 20
George Bush is inaugurated as 41st President of the United States

1990

February 28
Joint STARS reaches "Early Look" deployment

March
New JTIDS terminals are approved for initial production

March
MITRE Teleconferencing Center begins operations

Interlude Four

Expanding Capabilities
1986–1990

March
Strategic Air Command's new Command Center opens, completing eight years of MITRE work

April 10
MITRE reaches milestone on Strategic Defense Initiative, completes simulation work

June 5
Democratic elections in Poland bring Solidarity Party to power; Eastern Bloc begins rapid disintegration

November 9
Demolition of Berlin Wall begins

December
Robert Everett receives National Medal of Technology (the Nation's highest honor in Technology) from President Bush

December 20
MITRE supports Operation Just Cause in Panama

July 23
ABCCC III program begins accelerated 18 month upgrade

August 2
Iraq invades Kuwait; United States leads international coalition to curb further Iraqi aggression

1   The extremely sensitive radar antenna aboard Joint STARS aircraft can detect movement of ground vehicles at distances of hundreds of miles.

2   In the late 1980s, MITRE continued its original work in air defense, supporting the Air Force in development of the Iceland Air Defense System.

3   The company assisted the Environmental Protection Agency with documentation and technical analysis in the burgeoning Superfund program.

4   A prototype digital imaging system for U.S. Army doctors facilitated transmission, storage, and analysis of X-ray images.

5   The U.S. Navy's P-3 Orion, an aircraft used in anti-submarine warfare, features MITRE-engineered advanced communications and signal processing systems.

6   MITRE applied its expertise in secure, anti-jam communications in several generations of Have Quick radios.

Expanding Capabilities, 1986–1990

During the late 1980s and early 1990s, MITRE added formidable new capabilities in sophisticated information technology services for an array of government customers while maintaining traditional strengths in systems engineering and integration. Two primary factors stimulated this change. First, in the mid-1980s, federal spending on defense began a prolonged decline as the Cold War showed signs of winding down under new leadership in the Soviet Union. The thawing of East-West relations was prelude to the astonishing collapse of the centralized economies at the end of the decade—a momentous event in world history that completely changed the assumptions behind 40 years of investment in national security. In this new environment, MITRE's defense customers placed less emphasis on acquiring big new systems and more on enhancements and incremental technological change.

The second factor affecting the essence of MITRE's business was the accelerating revolution in information technology. During the company's first quarter-century, military requirements pushed the technological frontiers in computers and communications: ever faster processors with ever larger memories, yet packaged in ever smaller units; and major advances in signal processing, digital switching, digital networks, and satellite communications. By the 1980s, the commercial economy had discovered these technologies and began to push just as hard, and perhaps with greater speed. The gap between military and commercial development of information technology was narrowing, with the development of PCs, LANs, client-server architectures, centralized databases, and private information networks. In the late 1980s, many big corporations took advantage of these technologies to offer new products and services while also shrinking and streamlining their operations. These developments were not lost on high-level government officials, who saw the vast potential of new information technology to transform the nature of government operations and services.

Although MITRE continued to support big hardware programs in the pipeline—Joint STARS and upgrades to JTIDS and AWACS, for example—its newest assignments tended to focus on information management. Instead of developing wholly new systems, the company found itself increasingly preoccupied with making existing systems more efficient and capable, integrating older systems with newer ones, and integrating both into larger systems of systems. As a result, the company often also found itself working across organizational boundaries, as the systems it supported began to communicate and interact with systems developed elsewhere.

As these changes unfolded, MITRE began to develop new capabilities. Many of its new assignments still involved the challenge of making things work together that were designed to act independently—the original problem of SAGE. But many of these assignments proceeded under unfamiliar constraints that required new approaches. As government systems moved into spiral development patterns in which technology was continually refreshed or updated, MITRE grew more adept at managing this process and evaluating the results rapidly through experiments and prototypes. To insert commercial off-the-shelf (COTS) technology into government systems required the company to develop close links to information technology providers in the private sector. At the same time, as the government grew more concerned about the interconnectivity and interoperability of its disparate systems, MITRE gained significant experience and expertise in working across an array of programs and customers.

The company's status as an FFRDC remained invaluable during these changes in its business because its customers could depend on its advice without worrying about potential conflicts of interest. And as MITRE worked for more customers, its base of experience broadened and deepened—further enhancing its attractiveness to customers. The Army and Navy, for example, could benefit from MITRE's intimate knowledge of Air Force programs, while the Air Force could learn through MITRE new ways to meet technological challenges from the other branches. As with the military, so with civilian agencies, as MITRE's customers came to appreciate the company's diverse background and ability to capture and transfer learning.

Charles Zraket (l.) and Barry Horowitz presided over a major reorganization of MITRE in the late 1980s. In 1990, Horowitz succeeded Zraket, becoming the company's fifth president.

MITRE's ability to provide a range of information technology services developed over many years. The process, moreover, had no definite beginning—nor, as yet, a definite end. The mid- to late-1980s, however, represented a pivotal time. In 1986, Bob Everett reached retirement age and stepped down as MITRE's president. He remained a trustee until 1993 and is still an honorary trustee. Everett was succeeded by his long-time friend and colleague, 62-year-old Charles Zraket, whose distinguished career at MITRE included significant contributions to both its military and civilian government operations. He had served as a trustee since 1978 and as executive vice president and chief operating officer since 1984.

A former Director of Central Intelligence, Secretary of Defense, and Secretary of Energy, James Schlesinger became chairman of MITRE's board of trustees in 1986.

Facing page:

In the late 1980s and early 1990s, MITRE adopted a matrix organization structure that supported its operating centers with centers of specialized expertise in technology and management.

Given his age in 1986, Zraket's appointment represented a transitional step while the trustees searched for a longer-term successor. Among the internal candidates, the leading contender emerged as Barry Horowitz, who had risen quickly through the ranks in a series of increasingly responsible assignments in Bedford and Washington, acquiring familiarity with MITRE's customers on both sides of the house, military and civilian. In 1986, Zraket promoted the 43-year-old Horowitz to group vice president and general manager of the C^{3}I Group for Air Force Systems and a year later, in October 1987, to executive vice president and chief operating officer.

Everett's retirement coincided with a generational shift in MITRE's leadership, Zraket notwithstanding. During the next several years, many older officers and professional staff—James Croke, Edwin Key, Kenneth McVicar, Robert Mahoney, Alan Roberts, Alexander Tachmindji, and Norman Waks—left the company or phased into retirement. The new leadership team mixed insiders—Horowitz, Victor DeMarines, John Fearnsides, Richard Granato, Donald Neuman, Robert Nesbit, John Quilty, Cindy Spaney, and Lydia Thomas—with some outside hires—Gene Cross, Martin Faga, Larry Myers, and Harold Sorenson.

Meanwhile, during the early and mid-1980s, a host of veteran trustees stepped down, including Robert Charpie (chairman, 1972-1982), Edwin Huddleston, Jr. (a founding trustee), James Killian, Jr. (chairman, 1967-1969), William McCune, Jr. (chairman, 1982-1987), Courtland Perkins, Walter Roberts, Robert Sprague (chairman, 1969-1972), and Teddy Walkowitz. All of these men had built accomplished professional careers, but many had made their marks in law, business, or academia. In contrast, their successors constituted a "who's who" of U.S. national security leadership: Lewis Branscomb, formerly chief scientist at IBM and a professor at Harvard University's Kennedy School of Government; John Deutch, provost at MIT, formerly undersecretary of the Department of Energy and a future undersecretary in DOD and Director of Central Intelligence; Anita Jones, a professor of computer science at the University of Virginia and a future director of defense research and engineering; General Robert ("Tom") Marsh (Ret.), former head of the Air Force Systems Command; General Edward Meyer (Ret.), formerly chief of staff of the U.S. Army; William Perry, formerly a high-level DOD official and a future secretary of defense; James Schlesinger, formerly Director of Central Intelligence, Secretary of Defense, and Secretary of Energy; and Brent Scowcroft, a retired Air Force Lieutenant General, and a past and future national security advisor to the President. As chairman after 1987, Schlesinger proved a particularly prominent advocate for MITRE, helping to provide the company with access to government decision makers at the highest levels.

MITRE's Operating and Technical Centers

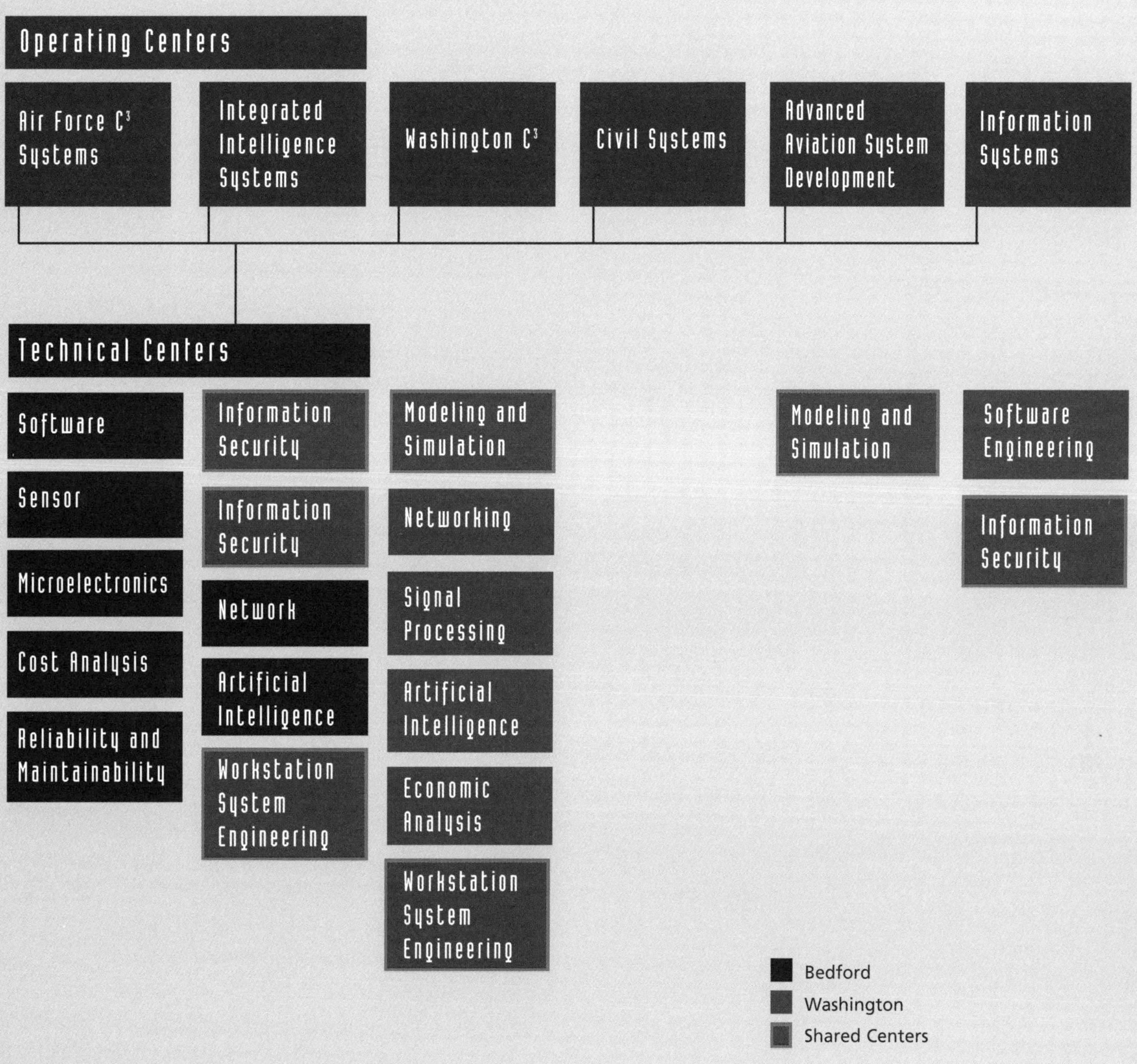

Operating Centers

Air Force C³ Systems	Integrated Intelligence Systems	Washington C³	Civil Systems	Advanced Aviation System Development	Information Systems

Technical Centers

Software	Information Security	Modeling and Simulation		Modeling and Simulation	Software Engineering
Sensor	Information Security	Networking			Information Security
Microelectronics	Network	Signal Processing			
Cost Analysis	Artificial Intelligence	Artificial Intelligence			
Reliability and Maintainability	Workstation System Engineering	Economic Analysis			
		Workstation System Engineering			

■ Bedford
■ Washington
■ Shared Centers

131. MITRE Corporation, Annual Reports for 1987 through 1992.

132. Lydia Thomas interview, November 4, 1997.

133. Barry Horowitz interview, September 5, 1997; MITRE Corporation, *Technical Centers at MITRE* (Bedford, Mass.: The MITRE Corporation, 1990), 1-6.

134. Ibid., 1.

Former Air Force Scientist Harold Sorenson joined MITRE in 1989 to lead the C³I group for Air Force Systems.

MITRE's new leaders presided over significant changes in the company's operations and organization, fostering expanded customer relationships in the intelligence community (*see Case 4*) and with the U.S. Army (*see Case 5*). The volume of MITRE's work for civilian government agencies also continued to grow under the Civil Systems Division, as Metrek was renamed in 1986. MITRE played an increasingly responsible role in support of the FAA's plan to modernize the National Airspace System (*see Case 6*). The company also opened up promising new areas of activity in civil systems.[131] For example, it provided advisory services to the military on the environmental implications of base closings and disposal of weapons and hazardous waste. According to one MITRE official, the company found innovative ways for the military to meet compliance standards at a savings of tens of millions of dollars.[132] Another major new area of activity involved law enforcement. In the late 1980s, MITRE reached a multi-year agreement with the Administrative Office of the U.S. Courts to serve as systems architect and provide acquisitions support for the development of a nationwide data communications network. MITRE also supported the Federal Bureau of Investigation to develop the National Crime Information Center, a database and associated systems to serve more than 62,000 criminal justice and law enforcement agencies in the United States and around the world.

In 1986 and 1987, the Zraket-Horowitz team initiated a major reorganization in its C³I operations. Starting with the C³I Group for Air Force Systems in Bedford, MITRE expanded on a fledgling matrix organization that had begun several years earlier and then spread this structure to Washington operations. The matrix involved the creation of a series of Technical Centers in areas such as sensors, software, local area networks, artificial intelligence, very high-speed integrated circuits, cost analysis, and reliability and maintainability. Their purpose was to improve the quality of service provided to major programs. The centers were each devoted primarily to a single technical discipline and, "to the extent practical," all staff practicing such a discipline on a day-to-day basis were assigned organizationally to the appropriate center. The other dimension of the matrix included the major projects and programs on which MITRE worked.[133]

The motive behind this change, according to a MITRE publication, was "the need to make more flexible and efficient use of our skilled personnel…Since our skilled staff are no longer embedded in various projects, we can more accurately gauge the strength of our skills and correct deficiencies." Other benefits claimed for the new structure included better quality control, improved training and development, and more economical use of facilities and equipment.[134]

During the late 1980s, MITRE also grew more conscious of the need to cultivate its base of experience and learning—to practice itself some of the innovations it counseled customers to adopt.[135] To facilitate the transfer of knowledge around the company and overcome organizational and geographical barriers between Bedford and Washington, MITRE expanded existing management policies and developed new techniques. The MITRE Institute, an organization founded to support technical training in 1973, was expanded significantly in the mid-1980s to consolidate an array of training and development activities across the company. Top management commissioned teams and study groups representing all parts of the company to investigate and share information about emerging issues and new technologies such as the Global Positioning System. The Systems Engineering Process Office documented procedures and innovations in project and program management, becoming a central repository of such information. The Risk Assessment and Management Program analyzed past programs and projects to interpret their results and identify lessons learned. MITRE also developed internal information systems and networks to facilitate the transfer of learning. These activities eventually blossomed in the establishment of the MITRE Information Infrastructure (MII), a Web-based intranet, in the early and mid-1990s.

By the close of the 1980s, MITRE seemed well along an evolutionary path from a company specializing in electronic systems, especially as required by the military, toward becoming a provider of high-level information technology services to both military and civilian government agencies. MITRE would continue along this path during the 1990s, although the scope of its activities would soon narrow following a fundamental debate about the company's mission.

135. Andrea Weiss interview, December 2, 1997; David Lehman interview, October 21, 1997; John Woodward interview, November 25, 1997; Cindy Spaney interview, August 15, 1997.

Computer FBCB2

Task Force XXI AWE Key Enablers

Communications
SINCGARS Improvement Program [SIP]

Position - Navigation
Precision Lightweight GPS
Receiver [PLGR]

Case Five Digitizing the Battlefield

Friend or Foe ID
Battlefield Combat Identification System [BCIS]

Communications
Enhanced Position Location Reporting
System [EPLRS VHSIC]

New information technology promises to transform the nature of combat, lifting the "fog of war," enabling faster tempos, increasing lethality of weapons, and reducing risks for friendly forces. In the 1990s, the U.S. Army launched its Force XXI initiative, harnessing new information technology in a broad effort to prepare itself for warfare in the next century.

As systems architect and engineer of Force XXI systems, MITRE has become a close partner with the Army. This partnership has deep roots in the company's work in information systems for the Department of Defense and its constituent services and organizations.

Pictured on overleaf: MITRE supports Force XXI by integrating systems for communications, identification, position reporting, and navigation to create a common picture of the battlefield.

Digitizing the Battlefield

The battlefield of the next century will bear scant resemblance to fields of combat made famous in history, where armies clashed at close quarters and casualties on both sides were likely to run high. Rather, future land battles may resemble the late stages of Operation Desert Storm, in which Allied ground forces overwhelmed Iraqi troops with hardly any hand-to-hand combat. Most of the fighting took place at a distance, as Allied air power first destroyed enemy positions and then Allied armor followed up. For an engagement of such scale, Allied casualties, including those caused by friendly fire, were remarkably, almost incredibly modest. The Allied troops were protected by an early version of an electronic shield that gave their commanders vastly superior situation awareness and enabled massive firepower to be directed with devastating effect from distances that kept most friendly forces out of harm's way.

Desert Storm provided a convincing demonstration of the power of information technology on the battlefield. Yet as MITRE chairman James Schlesinger observed, the weapons and systems unveiled in the Gulf War will never again catch an enemy by surprise. Maintaining America's technological advantage, he argued further, will require sustained investment and innovation.[136] Doing exactly that, the U.S. Army, the biggest branch of the military in terms of personnel, is betting on information technology to maintain its edge in the post-Cold War world.

The transformation of the Army into a fighting force for the early 21st century is a continuing process that reflects new doctrine, methods of training, technology and systems, and ways of working with contractors.[137] Along the way, the Army forged a new partnership with MITRE, drawn not only to the company's high level of technical expertise in information technology and systems integration and its trusted relationship with government and industry alike, but also to its familiarity with tactical and operational environments. MITRE's understanding of the Army's needs and requirements on the battlefield was demonstrated in the 1990s by its personnel on the ground with soldiers in Desert Shield/Desert Storm and Bosnia, but its roots trace back to the Vietnam War.

136. "James Schlesinger Says U.S. Risks Defense Decline," *Insight,* May 4, 1998, 23; Schlesinger, "Defense Budgeting and Planning: Raise the Anchor or Lower the Ship!" *The National Interest* (Fall 1997), 7-8.

137. Gordon R. Sullivan and James M. Dubik, "Land Warfare in the 21st Century," in Gordon R. Sullivan, *The Collected Works of the Thirty-second Chief of Staff United States Army: June 1991–June 1995* [Washington, D.C.?]: Dept. of the Army, [1996?], 179; U.S. Army Training and Doctrine Command, Force XXI: *Land Combat in the 21st Century,* (Ft. Monroe, Virginia, n.d.), 6–7.

Into the Foxholes

138. Victor A. DeMarines interview, August 12,1997; Richard S. Greeley, "Stringing the McNamara Line," *Naval History, July-August,* 1997, 60-66; Paul Dickson, *The Electronic Battlefield* (Bloomington, Indiana: University of Indiana Press, 1976), 83-97; Paul Edwards, *The Closed World: Computers and the Politics of Discourse in Cold War America* (Cambridge, Mass.: MIT Press, 1997),. 4–5.

139. Air Force History and Museums Program, Oral History Interview of Honorable John L. McLucas, April 10 and May 7, 1996, 2.

140. *MITRE: The First Twenty Years. A History of The MITRE Corporation, 1958–1978* (Bedford, Massachusetts: The MITRE Corporation, 1979), 114-115; Greeley, "Stringing the McNamara Line," 60; DeMarines interview, August 12, 1997.

MITRE first tested the electronic fence in the Panamanian jungle. (Facing the camera), Army Lieutenant General Alfred D. Starbird, Deputy Secretary of Defense for Defense Research and Engineering John S. Foster, and MITRE's David Israel.

In the summer of 1966, DOD Secretary Robert S. McNamara was concerned with the course of the war in Vietnam.[138] What had once looked like a small regional conflict that would quickly be resolved now showed signs of continuing almost indefinitely, at a high cost of American and Vietnamese lives, as well as huge financial outlays. A major problem was the relative ease with which the North Vietnamese and Viet Cong moved troops and supplies from the North into the South along routes such as the Ho Chi Minh Trail. Because much of the movement took place at night beneath a cover of dense jungle foliage, detection and inter-diction proved extremely difficult. Looking for ways to impede the enemy flow into South Vietnam, McNamara sought the advice of the JASON Committee, a high-level government scientific advisory study group drawn from universities, industry, and research organizations. The JASON scientists suggested that it might be feasible to build an "electronic fence" along routes frequented by the North Vietnamese and Viet Cong by dropping an array of acoustic and seismic sensors with built-in radio transmitters along these routes. The sensors would detect enemy movement and relay that information to an Air Force command post, which could then direct strike aircraft in for the kill. McNamara hoped to have the sensors in place by the fall of 1967, when the North Vietnamese were expected to make yet another push following the annual rainy season.

To oversee development of the proposed system, the DOD established a new entity, the Defense Communications Planning Group (DCPG), under Lieutenant General Alfred D. Starbird, formerly head of the Defense Communications Agency (DCA). Starbird was assisted by MITRE engineer David R. Israel, who took leave from the company to work for the DCPG.[139] Contracts were let with IBM, TRW, Sandia Corporation, Johns Hopkins, the Naval Research Lab, and other high-tech organizations. MITRE joined the effort as technical advisors to the DCPG, and its commitment eventually grew to about 50 professional staff. Led by Jack Dominitz, the company's work entailed general systems analysis, as well as testing and evaluation of components and subsystems.

Meanwhile, independently, another MITRE group worked directly for the Air Force on a related program called Igloo White, which was designed to build a SAGE-like radar system in Thailand that would not only help control air traffic in the region but also provide a linkage between the remote sensors and Air Force planes. Alan Roberts, Paul Sinesi, and Richard Fallows directed this work, which eventually resulted in MITRE's first field office in Southeast Asia. Frank Hopkins headed the office, which eventually became home to more than forty MITRE employees, including Richard Greeley and Vic DeMarines. The Bangkok office managed work on Igloo White and the new electronic fence.[140]

In January 1968, 16 months after start up, a string of sensors, the McNamara Line, was dropped along part of the Ho Chi Minh Trail and other supply routes frequented by the North Vietnamese and Viet Cong. The initial results were discouraging: many sensors failed to work, triggered inconsistently, or sent false alarms. It also proved extremely difficult to match up sensor inputs with meaningful target identification for U.S. aircraft, and despite extravagant claims of effectiveness that typified military public relations during the war, the number of successful attacks directly attributable to the system was negligible. Although the sensors eventually were made to work, the system did little to impede the flow of enemy forces and supplies or to influence the outcome of the war. It taught some valuable lessons, however. It especially underscored the promise of electronic systems on the battlefield, even as it also highlighted difficulties in making these systems operational and in establishing effective links between ground-based and airborne systems. "The technology was very, very exciting," recalls DeMarines,

we were doing all sorts of things…We had sensors. We knew who the truck driver was, where he came from, where he was going, and when he was going. But we couldn't hit him and we couldn't stop him. We had great intelligence information. We could tell everything, but then we'd just make holes in the sand because the technology wasn't balanced. We had great command and control but we didn't have an effective mechanism to follow up. That problem is solved today with precision deliveries, but in those days, there were just airplanes flying night sorties every ten minutes and occasionally hitting something. The next morning, the roads would be quiet because the trucks only moved at night. And the next night they would be back moving again.[141]

The experience of erecting the McNamara Line introduced a cadre of young military officers and contractors, including the MITRE contingent, to the challenges of building battlefield systems. One of these officers, Army Brigadier General John R. "Jack" Deane, would later become a key supporter of MITRE within the Army's high command. On the MITRE side, DeMarines credited the program for providing personnel with intimate knowledge of operational environments and a vivid sense of how the systems they designed and built were actually used in the field. The experience proved significant for a host of tactical programs, including JTIDS, and also helped the company broaden its military work beyond the Air Force.[142]

The immediate follow-on to the McNamara Line was an early-1970s program under joint DARPA and Army sponsorship called the Remotely Monitored Battlefield Sensor System (REMBASS). This system was designed to link sensors, communications, and display equipment and provide battlefield commanders with the capability for continuous, all-weather battlefield surveillance and target

Dropped from the skies above the Ho Chi Minh trail, sensors such as this one were designed to stick in the ground and relay information about enemy troop movements.

141. DeMarines interview, August 12, 1997.

142. Charles Zraket interview, October 22, 1997.

acquisition. This project led in turn to MITRE's involvement in bigger challenges: the integration of surveillance and other Army battlefield systems in development.

In the mid-1970s, top leaders in the Army, especially Jack Deane, now a four-star general and commander of the Army Materiel Development and Readiness Command, recognized that information technology could become a "force multiplier" to improve the quality and efficiency of U.S. troops without raising manpower levels. In 1975, the Army established its directorate for Battlefield Systems Integration, and the following year, it contracted with MITRE "for long-range assistance on its mission." In forging the relationship, General Deane was impressed by MITRE's experience in tactical Air Force operations, which represent the Army's biggest external area for integration, as well as its ability "to take a fresh look at Army problems and its general expertise on integration matters."[143]

In 1976, MITRE established the Battlefield Systems Division as part of its Washington Operations. The new unit managed a series of assignments "concerned with sensor systems to collect information on enemy movements and targets beyond the line of sight of friendly forces, communications and weapons to strike at such targets, means of suppressing enemy air defenses, and the overall architecture to tie these systems together."[144] One early program was called the Battlefield Exploitation Target Acquisition (BETA), an effort to gather data from battlefield sensors, correlate it with other information (including that generated by other services and friendly forces), and present commanders with displays to improve friend-foe identification and targeting. In 1977, the Army retained MITRE to provide systems engineering support and develop a test bed for correlating and displaying information. The success of the test bed initiative in 1981 led to the Joint Tactical Fusion Project, "an evolutionary multiservice effort to provide a coherent battlefield picture from correlated intelligence data that vary widely in accuracy, timeliness, and comprehensiveness."[145] The Army served as executive agent for the program, which MITRE supported as systems engineer.

Becoming a Partner

Meanwhile, the Army was finding MITRE's services valuable on other fronts. Since the early 1960s, the Army had worked with the company on the National Military Command System. Administered by the DCA and supported by MITRE as systems engineer, this program entailed the development of a communications system for the highest level of command and especially to ensure survivability of the system in the event of a nuclear attack. The program inevitably drew MITRE into contact with communications and computer specialists in every branch of the military and illustrated that the company was not simply an exclusive supplier to the Air Force.

143. The MITRE Corporation, *MITRE: The First Twenty Years*, (Bedford, Mass.: The MITRE Corporation, 1979), 182-183.

144. Idem.

145. MITRE Corporation, Annual Report for 1984.

Key personnel in the Battlefield Systems Division included (l. to r.) Jack Dominitz, John Quilty, Charles Joyce, Walter Yondorf, and William Woodward.

In the 1970s, MITRE's role in support of the World Wide Military Command and Control System (WWMCCS) obliged the company once more to work across organizational and service boundaries. (*See Interlude 3*.) The Army's participation in WWMCCS presented special challenges because the service lacked a technical support unit equivalent to MITRE for the Air Force or the several institutions that supported the Navy. After considering several options, the Army retained MITRE to help with the acquisition, transition, and implementation activities for WWMCCS systems unique to the Army. This support included "management planning, development and planning of acquisition strategy, technical monitoring of and assistance to contractors, development of software prototype and development strategies, and technical review of contractor deliverables and transition planning."[146]

Still another point of contact between MITRE and the Army was JTIDS. During the 1970s, the company worked on a hybrid between the Army-developed Position Location Reporting System and JTIDS, which became the Army's primary means for battlefield location and secure, anti-jam data communications in tactical settings. MITRE engineers helped write the specifications for the hybrid and carried out testing and evaluation. MITRE also designed interfaces between the hybrid and other tactical systems in development, including artillery fire control and anti-aircraft defense systems.

By the early 1980s, it was apparent to MITRE's top leadership in Washington—Charlie Zraket, Alex Tachmindji, and Ed Brady—that the Army represented a potential customer of major proportions in its own right. In 1982, Tachmindji tapped Rich Granato, a veteran of WWMCCS projects, as head of the Battlefield Systems Division. Assisted by Peter Freck, Granato spurred a significant expansion of business with the Army, especially to the Communications-Electronics Command (CECOM) at the headquarters of the Signal Corps at Ft. Monmouth, New Jersey. As information systems gained prominence in Army programs, CECOM assumed increasing responsibility for systems design, engineering, and procurement.

MITRE supported CECOM and other Army organizations around the world in a variety of programs. These included:

- An antiballistic missile program called Project Safeguard based in Huntsville, Alabama, which drew on MITRE's recognized expertise from the days of SAGE. On Project Safeguard, the company helped the Army evaluate data processing features of the system as well as survivability issues.[147]

- For U.S. forces stationed in Europe, MITRE provided systems engineering support for software and decision-making systems and helped design

146. MITRE Corporation, Annual Report for 1984, 21.

147. The MITRE Corporation, *MITRE: The First Twenty Years*, 121 and 181–182.

several command centers in Germany. These installations relied heavily on commercially available information technology.

■ MITRE provided "a top-level engineering description" of the design of the Army Tactical Command and Control System, helped design standards and protocols, and assisted with evaluation and acquisition of nondevelopmental hardware and software.[148]

By the late 1980s, more than 100 MITRE employees were working fulltime on Army programs around the world, with a growing concentration of activity at CECOM headquarters at Ft. Monmouth. In 1988, the MITRE board of trustees held one of its regular meetings at the Army's National Training Center at Ft. Irwin, California, where they reviewed company-supported systems in development. The following year MITRE relocated many Washington, D.C.-based personnel in the Battlefield Systems Division to a new installation at Ft. Monmouth. These two events illustrate a relationship between the Army and MITRE that was growing ever closer.[149]

In 1990, the Department of Defense realigned the structure of its sponsorship agreement with MITRE. The official sponsor of the company's defense-related FFRDC activities moved up from the Air Force to the Assistant Secretary of Defense for Command, Control, Communications, and Intelligence (C^3I). Within this context, the Air Force took responsibility for managing work on all its programs and projects—still by far the biggest area of MITRE's work—while the Army took responsibility for managing MITRE's work on all other DOD programs and projects. The change in sponsorship facilitated a process whereby MITRE's Washington C^3 Center, guided by John Quilty, was able to increase its work for the Army and Navy, even while the post-Cold War decline in size and budget of the Air Force led to reductions in MITRE's Air Force program.

During the next five years, under the energetic leadership of Harlan "Gene" Cross, MITRE's work at Fort Monmouth mushroomed, with almost 200 personnel dedicated to a host of Army projects. In addition, more than 100 MITRE staff under John Slaybaugh's direction supported other Army work. This growth reflected both the Army's growing appreciation of the company's expertise and capabilities and MITRE's efforts to focus its activities on programs of major significance to the Army. Victor J. Ferlise, the deputy to the commanding general of CECOM, valued the company for what he called its "profound knowledge" and expertise based on decades of experience in engineering and integrating complex systems, continuity on long-standing programs, and intimate familiarity with advanced electronic and information

In 1988, the growing volume of MITRE's work for the Army impressed trustees (l–r) Jack Ruina, Bob Everett, Paul Doty, Henry Loomis, and Tom Marsh.

Facing Page:

Early efforts to generate digital images of the battlefield illustrated potential to achieve dramatic improvements in situation awareness.

148. MITRE Corporation, Annual Reports for 1988 and 1989; Richard P. Granato interview, November 4, 1997.

149. Granato interview, November 4, 1997; Gene Cross interview, August 13, 1997.

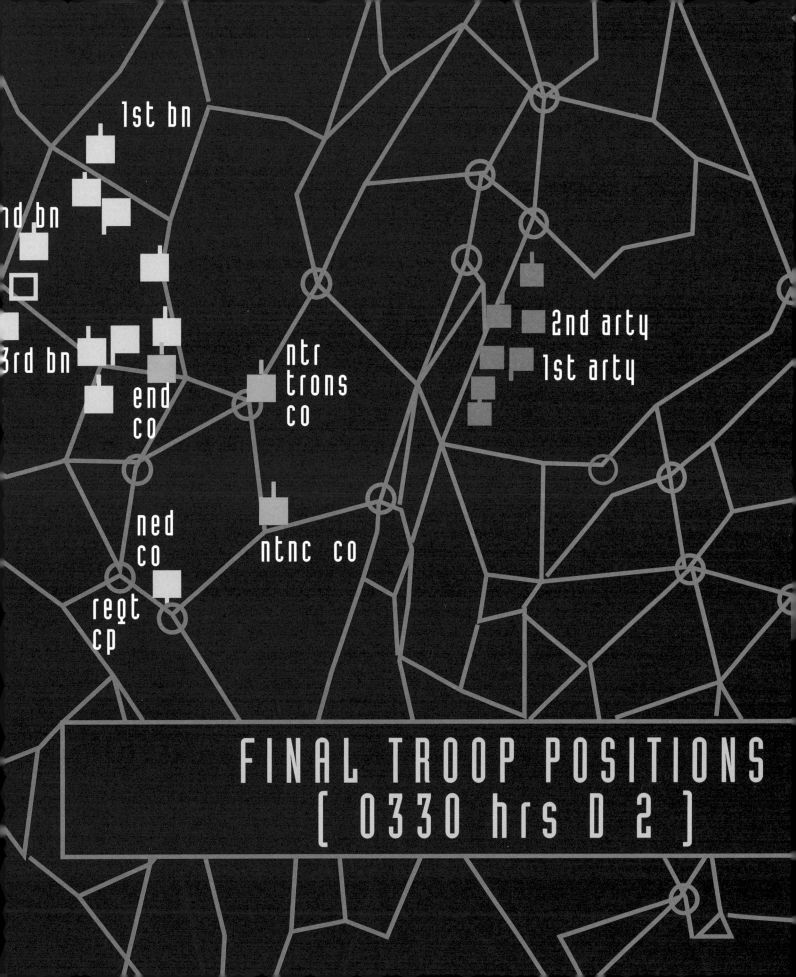

systems across the Department of Defense. For its part, MITRE repeatedly demonstrated its ability to manage complex technical problems for the Army in the areas of command and control, communications, intelligence, surveillance, and reconnaissance. In many instances, MITRE marshaled resources across the company on the Army's behalf through a process called "soft shelling," drawing in personnel from Bedford and Washington for specific assignments.[150]

During the early 1990s, the relationship between the Army and MITRE blossomed into a strategic partnership as the service undertook a sweeping effort to reinvent itself in the post-Cold War world.

Supporting the Army's Reinvention

Between the late 1940s and the early 1990s, much of American defense policy was premised on the possibility of confrontation between the United States and the U.S.S.R. Such confrontation could take many forms and occur in many places, but for any conflict short of an all-out nuclear exchange, the most likely scenario involved land battles along the East-West border in central Europe. To protect Western Europe from a devastating invasion, Soviet and East Bloc forces would have to be contained along this border by U.S. and Allied military forces. The assumptions behind this scenario shaped both Army doctrine and the deployment of troops for decades. In November 1989, the Army maintained 28 divisions, including 18 active and 10 in reserve; 24 of these were "committed, in one way or another, to fighting a war in Europe."[151]

In the late 1980s and early 1990s, a sequence of momentous events triggered a fundamental reassessment of the Cold War Army. The fall of the Berlin Wall in 1989 and the collapse of the Soviet Union two years later portended a "peace dividend" to American taxpayers in the form of lower spending on defense. Mounting concerns about federal budget deficits reinforced trends toward smaller budgets and more efficient use of government resources. At the same time, the spectacular performance of information-intensive weaponry during the Gulf War heralded the dawn of a new era of multinational cooperation and confirmed that a revolution was already under way in military affairs. And finally, the availability and growing use of low-cost and powerful commercial information technology was beginning to transform the functions and operations of corporations, nonprofit organizations, and government agencies.

These developments held far-reaching implications for the Army. Clearly, it would become smaller. Between 1990 and 1996, the Army reduced its total workforce by

MITRE opened its facility at Ft. Monmouth, New Jersey in 1989.

150. Victor Ferlise interview, December 22, 1997; Jason Providakes interview, December 22, 1997.

151. Gordon R. Sullivan and Anthony M. Coroalles, "The Army in the Information Age," in Sullivan, *Collected Works*, 396-407. The quotation is from 397.

463,000 soldiers and 133,000 civilians; it closed 674 bases around the globe and saw its budget slashed by 38 percent.[152] The new world order meant that the army would have to respond to more diverse threats around the world. It would be less likely to confront massive enemy forces fielded by another superpower and more likely to find itself facing a multitude of lesser threats: rogue military regimes, regions destabilized by ethnic conflict, and terrorists and drug lords wielding private armies. Future engagements would probably be small and focused, sometimes short, sometimes sustained—characteristics of "peace enforcement" rather than traditional warfare. Many of the Army's operations during the 1980s and early 1990s, including those in Grenada, Panama, the Middle East, Bosnia, and Somalia foreshadowed the shift. Many of these operations also illustrated the need for the Army to coordinate its activities not only with other branches of the U.S. military, but also with Allies and coalition partners.[153]

To prepare the Army for the future, General Gordon R. Sullivan, Chief of Staff (1991-1995), and General William W. Hartzog, head of the U.S. Army Training and Doctrine Command, directed the rewriting of basic doctrine to emphasize "power projection"—the ability to respond quickly and decisively to crises anywhere in the world from bases in the United States—as opposed to the "forward deployment" doctrine of the Cold War, in which American troops were stationed near probable sites of conflict. The new doctrine, in turn, led to new or modified weaponry, organizational designs, tactical concepts, and training and leadership development programs. The new Army would rely on information technology as a force multiplier and a facilitator of its doctrinal goals. It would also become a "learning organization," poised to experiment with new possibilities, learn from them, and incorporate its learning by continuously revising and improving its tactics and operations. This method of moving forward would enable government decision makers to make "both informed and supportable investment decisions in a declining budget environment."[154]

In light of the new doctrine, MITRE became an even more critical resource for the Army. The company participated in a host of new programs and initiatives during the early and mid-1990s. In 1994, the Army initiated a series of Advanced Warfighting Experiments (AWEs) to test the digitized battlefield, with close support from MITRE and commercial contractors. In 1994, for example, an AWE called Desert Hammer put "a battalion-sized digitized combined arms team" through a series of "constructive, virtual, and live" exercises, culminating in a two-week "live-fire and force-on-force operations" at the National Training Center.[155] More than 120 combat systems—tanks, Bradley Fighting Vehicles,

To understand how its systems operated in the field, MITRE's (l–r) Jeff Livesay, James Morris and Gene Cross went to the field.

152. William W. Hartzog and Susan Canedy, "21st Century Army," *Army* (February 1997), 23.

153. U.S. Army TRADOC, *Land Combat in the 21st Century*, 4.

154. Gordon R. Sullivan, "Leading Strategic Change in America's Army: The Way Forward," in Sullivan, *Collected Works*, 359; Brigadier General Steven Boutelle and Alfred Grasso, "Institutionalizing the Good Idea. A Case Study: The Central Technical Support Facility" (typescript, 1997), 1.

howitzers, command-and-control vehicles, and even individual soldiers—carried digital equipment that was fully or partially networked to generate a vastly more informative picture of the battlespace than previously attainable.

Desert Hammer demonstrated once more that new information technology could significantly improve situation awareness and also illustrated the power of simulations and interactive training techniques. Subsequent AWEs extended testing of the digitized battlespace in a variety of settings and involved bigger units and operations. Each of them underscored that "a close user, materiel developer, contractor working relationship is critical to success."[156]

In February 1995, General Sullivan established the Force XXI Campaign to guide the Army's continuing transformation. The five basic characteristics of the new Army included *"doctrinal flexibility, strategic mobility, tailorability and modularity, joint and multinational connectivity, and the versatility to function in war and operations other than war."*[157] In addition, Force XXI operations would have certain defining features. The "battlespace"—a term deliberately distinct from battlefield— would not only extend the dimensions of width, depth, and height so that smaller units could cover bigger areas, but it would also consider the electro-magnetic spectrum as part of contested terrain. New orders of precision and synchronous activity would characterize Force XXI operations. These activities could be centralized or decentralized depending upon circumstances. Finally, these activities would be coordinated with other U.S. services, allies, and coalition partners— an imperative soon to be reinforced by the Joint Chiefs of Staff in *Joint Vision 2010*, "the conceptual template for how America's Armed Forces will channel the innovation of our people and leverage technological opportunities to achieve new levels of effectiveness in joint warfighting."[158]

In 1995, the Army planned additional AWEs to test and evaluate Force XXI concepts. One of the most ambitious and challenging was "Task Force XXI," a brigade-level, force-on-force exercise scheduled for March 1997 at Ft. Irwin, California. MITRE supported Task Force XXI as systems architect and integrator. As described by Lieutenant General William Campbell, commander of the program office responsible for technical support to the AWE:

The whole intent of the endeavor is to improve the Army's ability to fight and win on the battlefield. Information technology, in that context, is viewed as an enabler. This technology will allow commanders to make better decisions, employing weapons systems to do their job better and faster, and soldiers who support the war fighters to do their jobs better...If we can distribute a common picture of the battlefield through information technology and if we can get everyone on the same sheet of music, then we can get all the deciders making the right decisions, and all the shooters into the fight, and all the support personnel aligned with the warfighting component. This includes providing anticipatory logistics, based on

As Army Chief of Staff, General Gordon R. Sullivan saw the revolutionary potential of information technology to transform warfare and the Army itself.

155. Units of the Army start with a platoon, consisting of up to ten people. Four platoons form a company; 4 companies form a battalion; 4 to 6 battalions form a brigade; 2 to 5 brigades form a division; and 2 to 4 divisions form a corps.

156. U.S. Army TRADOC, *Land Combat in the 21st Century*, 6–15. See also Sullivan, *Collected Works*, 324–325.

157. U.S. Army TRADOC, *Force XXI Operations* (Ft. Monroe, Virginia, August, 1994), 3–1. Italics in original.

158. Joint Chiefs of Staff, *Joint Vision 2010* (Washington, D.C., July 1996).

a common view of the battlefield, a common view of the plan, a common view of the terrain, a common view of the weather, a common view of friendly and enemy forces, and a common view of our courses of action and our current posture.[159]

Task Force XXI involved approximately 5,000 soldiers representing mobile units (infantry and armor), field artillery, engineers, intelligence, and special forces. These troops would have use of more than 70 electronic systems (produced by hundreds of contractors) that would be linked and made accessible through a wireless tactical internet, a commercially based data network conceived by members at the MITRE site. Among these systems, the "key enablers" were workstations; appliqués (portable computers—some commercially available, some specially ruggedized—that were attached to vehicles and weapon systems); several digital radio systems called SINCGARS (Single Channel Ground-to-Air Radio System); the enhanced position location representation system; commercially available, precision, lightweight GPS receivers; and a battlefield combat identification system. These systems were linked in the Army Battle Command System (ABCS), which could combine and display information from different sources in a variety of ways.

As plans for Task Force XXI took shape, the interoperability of the disparate battlefield systems was a major concern, while the use of wireless data communications on such a scale was unprecedented. Planners also recognized that there would inevitably be many bugs in the estimated four million lines of code constituting the software that drove and linked the systems. To help manage these concerns, Lieutenant General Campbell directed the establishment of a Central Technical Support Facility (CTSF) at Ft. Hood, Texas.[160]

MITRE's role in Task Force XXI ranged from the conceptualization and definition of the system architecture to the support of field integration and experimentation.[161] Under the overall direction of Fort Monmouth site leader Al Grasso, project leader Duane Christiansen, Lancz Griswold, and Jason Providakes developed a strawman support structure concept, including equipment requirements and layout of key facilities at the Task Force XXI Technical Support Cell, which housed the CTSF. MITRE also helped the Army in the initial period of integrating and assembling systems at Fort Hood. Finally, MITRE personnel led the overall test and integration effort of the ABCS.

In June 1996, a major test of systems integration at the CTSF revealed numerous technical problems, as well as inadequate training of personnel. When integration of components and systems had been tested in configurations of ones and twos, they appeared to work well. When it came time to scale up and integrate dozens

159. Lieutenant General William Campbell interview, November 3, 1997.

160. Col. Steven Boutelle, "Hot Wash for TF-XXI," undated presentation, [1996?], slide 3; Brigadier General Steven Boutelle, "Development of the Task Force XXI System Architecture," presentation, 22 October, 1997, slide 17; Providakes interview, December 22, 1997.

161. *MITRE Matters*, July 1, 1997.

of systems into higher-level systems, the Army ran into trouble: interconnectivity and interoperability problems; hardware and software that failed to meet specifications; poor documentation; and personnel under real-time operating pressures who quickly became frustrated at the problems they encountered.[162]

162. Campbell interview, November 3, 1997; Brigadier General Steven Boutelle interview, December 22, 1997; Providakes interview, December 22, 1997.

Opposite page:

MITRE's Steve Weiner works with Army personnel on test and integration activities at the Battlefield Visualization Laboratory at Ft. Monmouth.

This experience served as a wake-up call to the Army and resulted in revised procedures for moving ahead. The Army adhered to the original ambitious schedule—an AWE at Ft. Irwin within nine months—but General Campbell designated Colonel Steven Boutelle as "trail boss" to bring together teams representing the Army, MITRE, and major contractors to solve the technical and training problems. These parties shifted to a round-the-clock schedule and developed new implementation plans and procedures to get the exercise back on track. At General Campbell's request, Al Grasso dedicated top-level MITRE personnel to Task Force XXI, including specialists based in Bedford and Washington, as well as at Ft. Monmouth. Jason Providakes, who headed the effort, and other MITRE engineers uprooted and moved to Texas for the duration. The CTSF also took on an expanded role as a resource where Army personnel, MITRE engineers, and industrial contractors tested each step in the revised implementation plan in real time and in the presence of soldiers who would use the technology during the exercise. This method of working not only ensured that the systems worked but also, simultaneously, served as a means of training.

"As we went through that series of events of finding problems and finding fixes to the problems," General Campbell recalled, "MITRE played a central role in providing us with the technical support." Campbell added that MITRE

stood by its mantra that I would be buying the whole corporation when I bought a staff year. They provided some true experts who stayed with us down in Ft. Hood, and who worked with us around the clock. The time lines we faced were very short. The only thing that was not fungible, if you will, was the 24-hour day and the associated weekends. We worked 168 hours a week, instead of 40 hours a week. That meant putting multiple shifts down at Fort Hood. It meant overlapping shifts, so by and large we weren't on a 3-shift, 8-hours-per-day type of operation. Most people were working 12 to 18 hours a day, with overlapping shifts, the MITRE personnel included.

Boutelle came away impressed by MITRE's inventiveness during this grueling period. On one late-night visit to the CTSF, he found a handful of MITRE engineers writing software and piecing together commercial equipment into a system that could monitor and display the performance of the networks in the exercise. The resulting capability, called the Network Operations Center (NOC), first became available within 48 hours and it eventually proved an invaluable tool for tracking and evaluating how the systems were working—and for training soldiers to

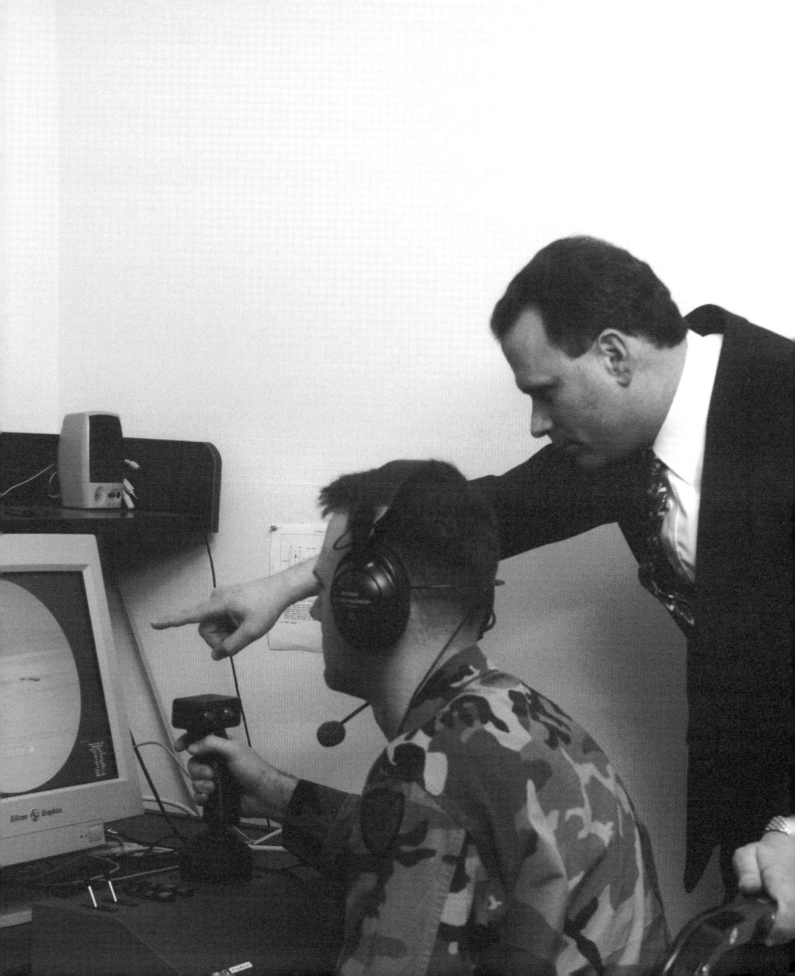

diagnose problems in the field. MITRE's role in developing the NOC capability had not been specified during the planning for Task Force XXI, nor was it formally part of the company's contractual responsibilities. Nonetheless, the NOC played a crucial role in developing the systems that supported the exercise.[163]

By the fall of 1996, the major systems integration and training problems appeared over. Campbell and Boutelle recognized, however, that the systems were hardly perfect and that "there were going to be work-arounds." In particular, they saw that some new components and software could not be fully tested and evaluated before the exercise. During the systems-integration phase, the CTSF had played this role; as Task Force XXI moved toward the actual AWE, the MITRE-contractor teams prepared to join the soldiers at Ft. Irwin to provide continuing technical support. Once again, the MITRE engineers relocated "out into the dust and sand and wind and rain and harsh weather in the high desert near Barstow California"— as Campbell described the setting:

163. Boutelle interview, December 22, 1997.

MITRE went to the desert with us. They lived with us in a facility that we called the bunkhouse because it was a real Army bunkhouse. That was in lieu of driving 35 miles back to town to stay in a hotel. Several people from MITRE stayed out there with us, and they worked around the clock with us. They also brought some network monitoring tools into the CTSF and were part and parcel of the infrastructure that changed the way we did business by shortening the cycle, by working with soldiers, by bringing new technology from the commercial sector on board from multiple sources, and by integrating that technology into an experimental force and helping us to train soldiers to use it. We compressed the cycle, so we could get the type of empirical data necessary in two years to make decisions that would have taken us five years if we'd gone through the traditional process.

The Task Force XXI AWE took place as scheduled at the end of March 1997. The Task Force XXI brigade, called the Blue Team, was equipped with the ABCS technology and other systems, while the opponent, the Red Team, used conventional technology and tactics. Permanently stationed at Ft. Irwin, the Red Team typically wins in training exercises because of its experience and knowledge of the terrain. This time proved no exception. But the Blue Team posted some noteworthy achievements. On the first day of training exercises, the Red Team almost always establishes a decisive advantage; during this AWE, the first day concluded with a stalemate. Throughout the exercise, the Blue Team proved able to control about twice as much geographical area as traditionally equipped brigades. On the other hand, although most systems including the integrated ABCS worked well, observers noted occasional problems of information overload. As Campbell put it, "there were some instances in which the data was so rich and the concepts so new that the soldiers spent so much time trying to get insight into what was happening on the battlefield that they weren't as agile and audacious as they might otherwise have been."

Overall, the Army's top brass interpreted the results of the Task Force XXI exercise as a resounding validation of new technology and concepts. Campbell and Boutelle believed that the spiral development process and the CTSF had cut the normal development cycle for new battlefield systems by three to five years. "We succeeded orders of magnitude beyond what the 'faint of heart' and the skeptics thought we could do," Campbell added.

We exceeded what even the optimists thought we could do. That's not to say that we had a perfect exercise, or that we had objective, mature systems. What it is to say is that we brought a number of technologies through a very rapid development and integration cycle; we integrated them horizontally with sufficient robustness that they could support a rigorous AWE; and we collected empirical data that allowed us to make judgments much earlier in the process than we ever could have under any other approach. We also found that the experiment gave us the opportunity to get data related to the human dimension and how soldiers would employ the equipment in the closest thing to real combat that we could use as a surrogate for actually going to war.

We could not have done it without MITRE's support and I am very grateful and personally indebted to some of the real heroes from MITRE who went to the desert, who stayed with us, and who made enormous contributions to Force XXI capabilities.

Boutelle—promoted to Brigadier General—paid a more succinct tribute to the company: its personnel "were committed. MITRE broke loose the experts. They delivered."

Following the brigade-level exercise in early 1997, the Army further tested Force XXI systems and concepts at the division level, and planned other exercises with the goal of giving the first divisions full digital capability during the year 2000. From there, other divisions will gain the capability in a planned sequence. Meanwhile, the Army's top officers began outlining the characteristics of the service beyond Force XXI, in a program called The Army After Next. Once again, information technology is expected to facilitate the Army's continuing transformation—and MITRE seems likely to be there to make a difference.

January 9
Joint STARS prototype aircraft are deployed to Persian Gulf

January 16
Persian Gulf War (Operation Desert Storm) begins. 20 of 40 MITRE divisions support Desert Shield/Desert Storm.

February 25
Warsaw Pact dissolves military alliance

February 28
Persian Gulf War concludes with Iraqi surrender and agreement to withdraw from Kuwait

Mosaic, first graphical interface browser, is developed at University of Illinois

January 17
MITRE President Barry Horowitz receives Air Force Exceptional Service Award for his leadership and MITRE's contributions during the Persian Gulf War

February
MITRE supports MAC in operation "Provide Hope" to airlift food/medical supplies to Russia

February 1
Presidents Bush and Yeltsin proclaim formal end of Cold War

March 1
I Lab (CAASD) achieves initial operating capability, becoming first facility to provide simulation in NAS modernization

April 13
Ron Grimm receives Air Force Air Medal for meritorious service aboard Joint STARS during Operation Desert Storm

October 9
United Nations creates Bosnia "no-fly" zone

December
U.S. troops deployed to Somalia for food relief effort

U.S. troops are deployed to Bosnia as part of NATO Joint Endeavor

January 20
Bill Clinton is inaugurated as 42nd President of the United States

March
Intel introduces 60 Mhz Pentium microprocessor

ARPAnet shuts down; first commercial Internet Service Provider (ISP), "The World" commences operation

October 1
Barry Horowitz becomes MITRE president

October 1
New sponsorship establishes the Assistant Secretary of Defense for C³I as primary sponsor of DOD FFRDC

October 1
FAA selects MITRE to operate new FFRDC

September 16
Soviet delegation of 30 high ranking military officials visits MITRE

October 30
NEXRAD (NEXt generation weather RADar) installation is dedicated

December 25
USSR dissolves into Commonwealth of Independent States (CIS)

1. Joint STARS aircraft in Europe for tests made valuable contributions to the Coalition victory in the 1991 Gulf War.

2. The Joint Worldwide Intelligence Communications System (JWICS) facilitated video conferences and other ways to share information across the intelligence agencies.

3. MITRE helped to develop the National Crime Information Center 2000 computer system for use by the FBI and other law enforcement agencies

4. In 1994 Group Leader Debra Galarowicz journeyed to Bosnia to install systems and train military personnel.

5. Between 1994 and 1996 MITRE supported the Ft. Franklin exercises at Hanscom Air Force Base to demonstrate and evaluate the latest command and control technologies.

1994

1995

1996

January
ROC/Taiwan Air Traffic Control modernization utilizes MITRE-designed system

January
MITRE recommendations for Eastern Europe airspace management are accepted by representatives from Hungary, Slovakia, Poland, and the Czech Republic

Joint Vision 2010 issued by Joint Chiefs of Staff

January 29
Victor DeMarines becomes president

January 29
MITRE Trustees elect to divide the company into two separate and independent corporations. MITRE retains FFRDC work for DOD and FAA; Mitretek Systems manages non-FFRDC government work

JTIDS becomes an integral part of Link 16

Army initiates "Advanced Warfighting Experiments" (AWEs)

April
MITRE engineers establish Intelink on nineteen servers for the intelligence community

July
NATO begins Operation Deny Flight, enforcing Bosnian "no-fly zone"

May 1
The MITRE Information Infrastructure (intranet) becomes operational

Interlude Five

Refocusing the Corporation
1990–1996

December
.North Warning System, replacing DEW Line, becomes operational

November 29
MITRE is asked to investigate "Year 2000" implications for DOD computer systems

December
ESC/Lincoln Lab/MITRE begin joint development of Cobra Gemini radar system

Refocusing the Corporation, 1990–1996

The year 1990 marked an important milestone in MITRE's constitutional history, encompassing major changes in the company's sponsorship agreements. First, recognizing the diverse nature of MITRE's customer base in defense and national security affairs, the Department of Defense revised the company's original sponsorship agreement. MITRE's primary sponsor became the Assistant Secretary of Defense for C^3I. Under this umbrella, the Air Force continued to sponsor MITRE's work for ESC and other Air Force commands, with the Army sponsoring MITRE FFRDC work for other defense customers.[164] Second, the Federal Aviation Administration moved to sponsor MITRE as an FFRDC to support modernization of the National Airspace System.

164. At the same time as the DOD revised MITRE's sponsorship agreement, it dropped the Federal Contract Research Center (FCRC) designation and replaced it with Federally Funded Research and Development Center (FFRDC).

165. MITRE Corporation, Annual Report for 1990.

These constitutional events were matched by important organizational changes at MITRE. The company divided its operations into two groups: the Bedford Group included the Air Force C^3 Systems Center and the new Center for Intelligence and Special Programs; the Washington Group consisted of the Washington C^3 Systems Center, which worked on C^3 systems for DOD customers outside of the Air Force; the Center for Advanced Aviation System Development (CAASD—the new FAA FFRDC); and the Center for Civil Systems, which carried on the company's support for civilian government agencies. To oversee this structure and lead MITRE, the board elected Barry M. Horowitz as president and chief executive officer succeeding Charles Zraket, effective October 1, 1990.[165]

Horowitz took office during a time of profound change for MITRE and its customers. Many of the assumptions behind U.S. foreign, defense, and national security policies since the late 1940s seemed suddenly obsolete. The Cold War was effectively over, with the disintegration of the Eastern Bloc, the destruction of the Berlin Wall, the pending reunification of Germany, and the imminent collapse of the Soviet Union. These developments reshaped national borders and political alignments around the world. They also reinforced sentiments across the United States for additional cuts in defense spending, which had already been drifting downward since the mid-1980s. The onset of a deep recession in the United States in the early 1990s heightened concerns about the magnitude of the federal budget deficit and portended still more cuts in government programs. Throughout the aerospace and defense industries, including at MITRE, there was marvel and rejoicing at the end of the Cold War, but also concern about future roles and responsibilities in a radically new geopolitical context.

Three months before MITRE's change of command, another momentous event demonstrated the dimensions of the new world order and afforded glimpses into the future of warfare and government operations. The Iraqi invasion of Kuwait on August 2, 1990 triggered a response of unparalleled international cooperation. Most countries around the world supported—or, at least, declined to oppose—a coalition of United Nations forces led by the United States against the aggressors. When Operation Desert Shield (intended to contain further Iraqi expansion) escalated early in 1991 into Operation Desert Storm (designed to force Iraqi withdrawal from occupied territory), the Allied coalition unleashed a dazzling variety and overpowering volume of advanced military technology. The result was swift, decisive, and an overwhelming validation of new C³I and weapons systems and new military tactics based on joint operations involving air, land, and sea forces and units representing many different nations.

MITRE systems and personnel played key roles in supporting coalition forces during Desert Shield and Desert Storm, especially via the C³I systems it had helped develop. In all, 12 of the company's 20 technical divisions played a part, engaging personnel in U.S. installations and deployed at several locations near the Persian Gulf. MITRE worked with the Defense Information Systems Agency to establish "the largest integrated, commercial long-haul military network ever implemented." This network helped coordinate communications between Washington and Saudi Arabia and between and among U.S. forces and their allies. The Airborne Battlefield Command and Control Center III (ABCCC-III) facilitated a variety of tactical missions and helped control air attacks against Iraqi ground forces. AWACS aircraft provided yet another convincing demonstration of command and control of the skies, providing "continuous coverage of the air picture from the Red Sea to the Persian Gulf" throughout the conflict. In addition to detecting movement of enemy aircraft, AWACS helped to manage traffic of the thousands of coalition aircraft in the theater.[166]

Perhaps the most spectacular illustration of MITRE-engineered technology in Desert Storm was the performance of the Joint Surveillance Target Attack Radar System (Joint STARS or JSTARS). This joint Air Force/Army program had originated in the early 1980s with programs at Lincoln Lab and at Rome Air Development Center and used extremely sensitive airborne radars and advanced information technology to identify and track movement of ground vehicles at

166. Thomas A. Keaney and Eliot A. Cohen, *Gulf War Air Power Survey Summary Report* (Washington, D.C.: U.S. Government Printing Office, 1993), 192–194; Stuart H. Starr, "C3I for Coalition Warfare: Lessons Learned from Desert Shield/Desert Storm," undated MITRE typescript; MITRE Corporation, Annual Report for 1991.

ranges of many miles. In effect, Joint STARS was designed to provide a picture of distant ground activity similar to the image of distant air activity that AWACS made possible. MITRE supported the Joint STARS program in its familiar role as systems engineer for design, analysis, and testing. Late in 1990, two development Joint STARS aircraft performed successfully in European field operations demonstrations, and General H. Norman Schwartzkopf, commander of U.S. forces in the Gulf, requested that these aircraft be deployed in support of Desert Storm.

The two prototype Joint STARS aircraft arrived in the Gulf days before the beginning of the air war in January 1991. The systems and equipment were so new that military personnel had not been trained to operate them, so civilians, including MITRE's Ron Grimm (later a recipient of the Air Force Air Medal) were pressed into duty. The aircraft flew 55 missions, and one of them was in the air every night of the war. Joint STARS provided reconnaissance of Iraqi ground forces and helped detect an abortive Iraqi incursion into Saudi Arabia designed to precipitate a land battle in the early days of the war. The system also helped to track and target mobile Scud missile launchers. Throughout the conflict, Joint STARS provided a stream of targeting information to ABCCC-III, AWACS (via a new, MITRE-developed prototype JTIDS terminal) and strike aircraft.[167]

The lop-sided coalition victory in the Gulf underscored the enormous significance of information technology for modern warfare. Such technology facilitated vastly superior situation awareness, tight coordination among branches of the military and allied forces, and weapons systems of extraordinary precision and devastating effect. The revolution unfolding in military affairs reflected a more general transformation of government generally, as information technology helped reshape operations in both military and civilian sectors.

The potential to "re-invent" government reinforced optimism at MITRE about the future, but in the near term, not long after the Gulf conflict, leadership at the company confronted difficult strategic choices. The collapse of the communist bloc raised basic questions about the mission and continuing existence of organizations like MITRE, which had originated in a Cold War context, and provided fresh ammunition to long-time critics. Some opponents of FFRDCs wondered whether there was any longer need for such institutions. At the same time, organizations such as the Professional Services Council, a lobbying group that represented private government contractors, escalated their arguments against the special relationship between FFRDCs and their sponsors, asserting that the relationship was inherently costly and inefficient and a burden no longer

167. Keaney and Cohen, *Gulf War Air Power Survey Summary Report,* 109–110 and 192–193; Harold Sorenson interview, October 1, 1997; MITRE Corporation, Annual Report for 1991.

Facing page:

For Operation Desert Shield in 1990, MITRE engineered significant improvements to the U.S. military's Global Transportation Network, facilitating rapid deployment of troops and materiel to the Persian Gulf.

warranted in an era of tight budgets. The Professional Services Council and its allies and supporters in Congress also claimed that competitive organizations could match the services of the FFRDCs at lower cost.[168] They further argued that MITRE was using its FFRDC status to obtain non-FFRDC work unfairly. MITRE and its supporters strongly rejected such arguments.

MITRE initially withstood these attacks and the decline in military spending because many of the programs that engaged it were shielded in R&D budgets that were cut proportionately less than other areas of the overall defense budget. The company's leaders knew, moreover, that the impact of spending cuts on programs in development would not show up for several years.[169] Finally, the company continued to diversify its customer base, with additional work for the intelligence community, the U.S. Army, and some civilian agencies. Nonetheless, MITRE felt the impact of ceiling cuts and staffing caps on Air Force and other DOD programs. The company's contract revenues began to level off in 1992 and peaked the following year at about $600 million, and then began to slide, to $592 million in 1994 and to $576 million the following year. Total full-time employment also dropped, from a record high of more than 6,000 in 1990 to just under 5,000 in 1995.[170]

In addition to the short-term pain that falling revenues induced, Horowitz recognized that MITRE was once more back in a situation—he called it a "crisis"— similar to that in the mid-1960s, before the company had formulated its initial diversification strategy. In an era of increasing competition for information technology experts, MITRE risked losing key employees and seemed likely to face serious problems in recruiting high-quality personnel, offering them attractive career opportunities and financial security, and providing for organizational renewal. The difference between the 1960s and the 1990s was that the government was no longer expanding, competition among service providers was intensifying, the distance between military and commercial technology was closing, and criticism of FFRDCs was rising. In these circumstances, Horowitz believed he saw a way out. He proposed that MITRE set up a separate, profit-making subsidiary that would draw on the company's vast expertise in information systems for commercial purposes. As a pioneer in systems integration, the company seemed ideally poised to capitalize on the booming growth of new technologies such as the Internet. Why not sell the capabilities that developed Intelink and other government systems on the outside? There were many profitable opportunities to be exploited in a for-profit subsidiary. If the plan should be successful, then MITRE would open up career opportunities for its personnel. At the same time, the subsidiary's profits could serve as an endowment to ensure MITRE's long-term survival and renewal.[171]

168. For a summary of criticism of FFRDCs, see U.S. Senate, Subcommittee on Oversight of Government Management, *Inadequate Federal Oversight of Federally Funded Research and Development Centers,* July 8, 1992; see also Sandra Sugawara, "The Mighty Voice of MITRE," Washington Post, August 20, 1989, H1 and H6.

169. Barry Horowitz interview, September 5, 1997; MITRE Corporation, *Use of MITRE in the DOD,* White Paper, March 1991, 5.

170. MITRE Corporation, Employee/Officer Statistics, 1965–1994, undated document in Corporate Archives; MITRE Corporation, Annual Report for 1995.

171.Horowitz interview, September 5, 1997.

The plan to launch a for-profit subsidiary proved controversial among MITRE executives and technical personnel who feared that the company would compromise its mission to serve the public interest and jeopardize its hard-won reputation as a provider of objective advice to the government. During 1995, proponents and opponents of the plan inside the company engaged in spirited debates about the plan's merits and drawbacks. Opinion was also divided among the trustees, who nonetheless authorized the company's leaders to discuss the plan with its sponsors.[172]

172. James Schlesinger interview, November 4, 1997; Jack Ruina interview, October 14, 1997; and Lewis Branscomb interview, November 24, 1997.

Officials in the DOD understood the dilemma the company faced, but they were skeptical of the proposed remedy. They registered several concerns. First and most important, they pointed out that MITRE had been established to carry out a mission that still needed performing: to provide high-quality technical advice to the government, especially in the area of C^3I systems. From the DOD perspective, there remained plenty of work for MITRE to do. In fact, they expected to make intensive use of MITRE's services as the military and other DOD sponsors adapted to new budgetary circumstances and relied on information technology to become more efficient. DOD officials worried, therefore, that a separate subsidiary at MITRE could dilute the company's focus and divert management attention from its core mission. Another concern was that the proposed arrangements would set a precedent for other FFRDCs that, once admitted, would be difficult to reverse. Finally, the DOD argued that allowing the FFRDCs to set up competitive organizations, no matter how structurally distinct, would make them even more vulnerable to attacks from industrial contractors and legitimize concerns about government favoritism and FFRDC conflicts of interest.

In the end, the DOD officials did not presume to tell MITRE what to do, but they indicated a change in policy that gave the company little choice but to rethink its future options. The policy change would reverse arrangements governing work performed outside of the sponsorship agreement by FFRDCs that had been set up following the Currie Plan in 1976. (*See Interlude 2.*) At that time, the DOD had abandoned procedures that called for sponsors in effect to grant waivers each time an FFRDC wanted to undertake a project that fell outside the sponsorship agreement. This step had enabled MITRE to seek work from non-DOD agencies without first seeking the DOD's approval. In 1995, however, DOD officials were prepared to acknowledge criticism of these arrangements from industrial contractors, who argued that the FFRDCs used their favored position with sponsors to subsidize diversified activities.

The change in DOD policy put MITRE in an untenable position. Each time it wanted to undertake a new project for the FBI, the GSA, or any other civilian agency besides the FAA, it would first have to obtain DOD approval. Not only would such a process be time-consuming, it would also be risky: MITRE could not guarantee its customers that it would be permitted to perform the work proposed.

In these circumstances, top executives and trustees reassessed their alternatives. Horowitz, who had campaigned hard for the subsidiary and continued to believe in its merits, was reluctant to give it up. At the same time, it was clear that MITRE could not risk alienating its biggest FFRDC sponsor. During November and December, a new plan quickly took shape. MITRE would retain its two FFRDCs and spin off virtually all of its other businesses—principally the Center for Environment, Resources, and Space and the Center for Information Systems—into a new, completely independent, not-for-profit corporation. This new corporation, eventually called Mitretek Systems, would then be free to test the idea of the separate subsidiary. Horowitz resigned from MITRE to become president of Mitretek and later its new subsidiary, named Concept Five Technologies. A number of long-time MITRE officers and employees, including Dr. Lydia Thomas, who succeeded Horowitz as president of Mitretek Systems, Richard P. Granato, who joined as executive vice president, and Dr. John M. Ruddy, formerly vice president of the DOD FFRDC, accompanied him. In addition to Horowitz, three trustees, including Charles Zraket, also left MITRE to cast their lot with the new organization.[173]

The separation took effect in January 1996 but working out the details—the division of assets, the apportionment of overhead costs, the untangling of integrated systems—consumed many months. MITRE gave up about $75 million in contract revenues in non-FFRDC work and approximately 800 people. The company retained contract revenues of about $454 million and employment of approximately 4,000 people.

As MITRE's new president and chief executive officer, the trustees elected 58-year-old Victor A. DeMarines. A thirty-year veteran of the company, DeMarines had worked his way up through many assignments, including the McNamara Line (*Case 5*), JTIDS (*Case 3*), and many projects for the intelligence community (*Case 4*). The leadership of the company's biggest units—Hal Sorenson at the Center for Air Force C^2 Systems, John Quilty at the Washington C^3 Center, Marty Faga at the Center for Integrated Intelligence Systems, and Jack Fearnsides at the Center for Advanced Aviation System Development—remained in place. Larry

173. Horowitz interview, September 5, 1997; Lydia Thomas interview, November 4, 1997; Richard Granato interview, November 4, 1997.

A special issue of *MITRE Matters* in 1996 announced the impending split of the company into two pieces: the DOD and FAA FFRDC work remained part of MITRE, and all other activity shifted to a separate company that would become Mitretek Systems.

Myers continued as senior vice president and chief financial officer, and Gene Cross as senior vice president and operations officer with oversight of the company's central operational functions and responsibility for implementing the separation of the two companies.

Throughout the debates and discussions that led to the split of the company, MITRE continued to meet its primary responsibilities to its customers. For the FAA, it forged ahead with modernization of the nation's system of air traffic control. (*See Case 6.*) For DOD, the company provided technical assistance to existing programs such as AWACS and Joint STARS and helped advance newer projects such as Intelink and the combat systems of the Army's Force XXI initiative. MITRE also helped to define emerging new DOD priorities such as information warfare and infrastructure protection. And MITRE personnel continued to work with its customers in the field. During Operation Joint Endeavor, the coalition peacekeeping mission in Bosnia-Herzegovina, MITRE engineers helped develop and integrate a variety of intelligence systems to support military commanders. Group Leader Debra A. Galarowicz, for example, braved land mines and sporadic fire from snipers during a 31-day march through Bosnia to upgrade software and train military personnel in the use of the Theater Rapid Response Intelligence Package. Along with three MITRE colleagues, Galarowicz received a special citation from the U.S. Army for "making significant contributions to Operation Joint Endeavor."[174]

174. "Debra Galarowicz Travels through Bosnia and Herzegovina to Aid TRRIP Users," *MITRE Matters*, February 1997; "MITRE Brings Technical Expertise to Peacekeeping Effort in Bosnia-Herzegovina," *MITRE Matters*, December 1996. "Army Honors MITRE Personnel in Germany," *MITRE Matters*, August 1996.

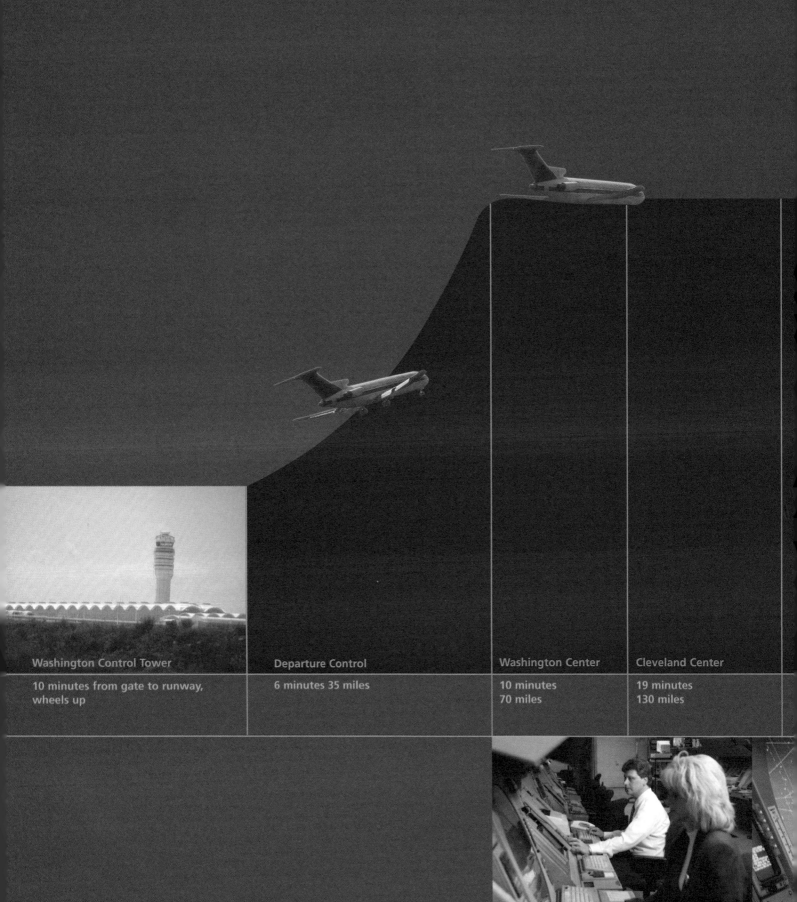

Washington Control Tower

10 minutes from gate to runway, wheels up

Departure Control

6 minutes 35 miles

Washington Center

10 minutes
70 miles

Cleveland Center

19 minutes
130 miles

Indianapolis Center	Chicago Center	Approach Control	Chicago Control Tower
23 minutes 160 miles	24 minutes 168 miles	15 minutes 50 miles	10 minutes Includes taxi time to gate

Case Six

Toward a System of Collaborative Air Traffic Management

A paradigm shift is under way in managing U.S. airspace. The traditional approach to air traffic control based on separation assurance and flow control is giving way to Collaborative Air Traffic Management. Under the new approach, FAA service providers and flight operators collaborate to make decisions about routes and schedules. The resulting savings, say some experts, may total $3 billion per year or more.

Engineering improvements to FAA systems is a highly complex problem that requires not only familiarity with the state of the art in information technology, but also sensitivity to the interests of stakeholders in the system: the flying public, the FAA, and operators of airlines, freight services, and general aviation aircraft. MITRE has worked with these parties since the beginnings of automation in air traffic control in the late 1950s and is now helping to implement the systems and decision-support tools that will realize Collaborative Air Traffic Management.

Pictured on overleaf: A flight between Dulles Airport near Washington, D.C and Chicago's O'Hare Airport is monitored and controlled by FAA systems at both airports and at control centers along the route. With MITRE's support, these systems are evolving in ways to increase safety and flexibility for both users and managers of the airspace.

Toward a System of Collaborative Air Traffic Management

When MITRE was created in 1958, the eventual revolution in military capabilities that SAGE would spawn lay far ahead in the future. At the time, however, experts readily saw that the problem of continental air defense bore marked similarities to that of controlling commercial air traffic. Soon after its founding, MITRE began supporting civilian authorities in the automation of the National Air Space (NAS), and over the years became a significant resource to the Federal Aviation Administration (FAA). In 1990, the close partnership between the agency and the company was formalized in an agreement in which the FAA established MITRE's Center for Advanced Aviation System Development (CAASD) as an FFRDC with special responsibility for systems architecture.

In many respects, MITRE's role as partner and systems architect to the FAA is a natural reflection of its mastery of the technologies central to management of the NAS. After all, the U.S. system of air traffic control represents the biggest and most successful continuously operating command and control system in the world. Yet developing and upgrading a complex system in which many parties—government officials, air traffic controllers, pilots, dispatchers, traffic flow specialists, and the flying public—have big stakes have been fraught with challenges from the beginning. These challenges are partly technological and partly organizational, involving not only sophisticated information technology but also balancing the needs, interests, and concerns of many organizations and groups.

These twin aspects of managing the NAS—the technological and the organizational—are captured in a new approach of the late 1990s called Collaborative Air Traffic Management, a term distinctly and deliberately different from the traditional function of air traffic control. The new approach emphasizes enhanced decision-support tools for FAA service providers and flight operators in the NAS to bring about a new order of collaboration between and among these parties. Collaborative ATM is intended to give flight operators more of a voice in scheduling and routing decisions, with resulting savings in time and fuel costs. Using currently available technologies, the air traffic management system of the early 21st century will be safer than today's system, yet more flexible, economical, and convenient for all parties.

MITRE is helping lead the way to this new era in partnership with the FAA. This partnership has deep roots. Since the late 1950s, with some ebbs and flows, MITRE has worked continuously with the FAA on the design and improvement of the NAS, as well as on the development of new air traffic concepts, from automated data processing in the early days, to new decision-support tools for controllers in the 1970s and 1980s, to the emergence of Collaborative ATM in the 1990s.

The Shaping of a System

On June 30, 1956, a United Airlines DC-7 and a Trans World Airlines Constellation, both flying eastward out of Los Angeles, collided in mid-air, at 21,000 feet over the Grand Canyon. Everyone aboard both aircraft—128 people—perished. At the time, it was the worst air disaster in U.S. history, and it highlighted the need for a better approach to air traffic control.[175]

At the time, air traffic control relied on a combination of ground-based radar to locate and confirm aircraft position and voice communication for information about identity and flight plan. A flight crew was responsible for radioing periodic reports to ground controllers situated at airports. Controllers then recorded this information in coded form, identifying aircraft on clear plastic markers called "shrimp boats" and moving these by hand across a horizontal radar display. The controllers' challenge was to keep each marker close to the radar "blip" corresponding to its moving aircraft so that the identity of each aircraft would remain clear. Although adequate at the time it was invented, the system was sorely taxed by explosive growth of air commerce in the 1950s. At a given moment, a controller might have to keep track of dozens of shrimp boats, often running out of room on the radar displays. At the same time, the controllers wrote supplementary flight information, such as time estimates, on flight progress strips mounted in racks near the radar display. During peak traffic periods, maintaining an accurate mental picture of the situation was extraordinarily difficult.[176]

During the early and mid-1950s, as the Air Force and Lincoln Laboratory developed SAGE, civilian authorities saw the potential to marry radars and computers for real-time tracking and management of civilian air traffic. A number of studies were under way when the Grand Canyon tragedy precipitated congressional action. The Federal Aviation Act of 1958 established the Federal Aviation Agency (FAA, renamed as the Federal Aviation Admintration when it became part of the Department of Transportation in 1967), with "sole responsi-bility for developing and maintaining a common civil-military system of air navigation and air traffic control."[177]

Supervising air traffic in the era before computers required controllers such as these at Boston's Logan Airport in 1960 to keep track of flights by using handwritten paper strips.

175. Michael S. Nolan, *Fundamentals of Air Traffic Control* (Belmont, Cal.: Wadsworth Publishing Company, 1994), 24–25.

176. "Air Traffic Control: Looking Toward the Next Generation," MITRE Matrix, Vol. 3, No. 4 (July-August 1970); MITRE Corporation, *MITRE: The First Twenty Years* (Bedford, Mass.: The MITRE Corporation, 1979), 76.

177. Federal Aviation Administration, *An Overview of the Federal Aviation Administration,* undated electronic document.

These events coincided with the birth of MITRE and the movement of SAGE into an operational phase. The company's growing mastery of radar, real-time control systems, and depiction of the airspace had obvious appeal to the FAA. In 1959, the FAA joined with the Air Force in funding the SAGE-Air Traffic Integration (SATIN) program to build a semi-automated air traffic control system across the United States. (*See Interlude 1.*) Developed by a team of MITRE engineers including David R. Israel, SATIN used computers to process data relayed by airborne "beacons" (automatic transponders) that continuously reported an aircraft's identity and altitude. These data were then combined with inputs from radar for display on controllers' terminals. In addition to locating aircraft, SATIN also helped identify and correct pilot and controller errors, update flight information, process flight plans, display weather conditions, and coordinate and transfer flight control automatically between controllers in adjacent facilities. During the next several years, MITRE modified a SAGE installation in Great Falls, Montana, to demonstrate SATIN's feasibility.[178]

Meanwhile, on December 16, 1960, a second, tragic mid-air collision, this time over New York City, again focused public attention on the limitations of existing air traffic control procedures. The following March, newly elected President John F. Kennedy directed FAA Administrator Najeeb Halaby to "conduct a scientific, engineering overview of our aviation facilities and related research and development and to prepare a practicable long-range plan to insure efficient and safe control of all air traffic within the United States." In response, Halaby appointed a task force, which took the name, Project Beacon.[179]

After nearly a year reviewing procedures and initiatives under way, the Project Beacon task force issued its final report and recommendations in early 1962. The report found that much R&D work to improve air traffic control was focused on advanced radars, computers, and systems originally designed for air defense and that not enough attention was paid to near-term concerns of civilian controllers in the field. The report recommended against further attempts to integrate military air defense programs and civilian air traffic control as prohibitively expensive and unnecessary. Instead, it called for expeditious development of a new civilian air traffic control system, eventually known as the NAS. The system would establish a network of Air Route Traffic Control Centers (ARTCCs) across the country and link them to radar-equipped terminal approach control facilities at or near airports. It would accept and store flight plans, distribute and update them automatically, and facilitate the transfer of flight plan information from one control center to another as an aircraft moved along its journey. The old system of separate radar screens and manual shrimp boats

178. Early algorithm development and specifications show SATIN attempted very modern air traffic management functions like an automated strategic conflict probe, but the computers of the era were unequal to the task.

179. The account in this paragraph and the next several relies on Nolan, *Fundamentals of Air Traffic Control*, 27–29 and 346–347.

In 1961, the SAGE-Air Traffic Integration (SATIN) program helped to automate air traffic control.

would be scrapped and, as demonstrated in SATIN, new display terminals would enable controllers to combine radar inputs with data from airborne beacons and continuously updated flight plans on a single screen.

As SATIN wound down, MITRE's support to the FAA dipped from 45 to 24 staff years between 1961 and 1966. Despite this decline, the FAA continued to value the company's technical expertise and objectivity, and in 1963 it asked MITRE to establish a site in Washington to provide systems engineering support in developing the NAS. That summer, MITRE moved a contingent of personnel from Bedford to Washington, where they joined with staff supporting the Defense Communications Agency (*see Interlude 1*) to form the company's Washington Operations. As directed by David Israel and Howard Kirshner, much of MITRE's initial work on the NAS focused on the Northern Tier Integration Project (NOTIP), the first operational program to use computers and digital data for air traffic control. Installed in three SAGE direction centers, NOTIP facilitated testing and evaluation of new procedures and equipment.

As the NAS began to take shape and moved toward acquisition and operation in the late 1960s, the FAA sought an increasing level of technical assistance from MITRE.

Developing the National Airspace System

Project Beacon had envisioned a single flight data processing system that would perform all of the essential functions of air traffic control throughout a given flight, from take-off to landing. As work on the NAS proceeded, however, it became clear that the differing requirements of en route control and terminal control necessitated developing two separate radar-beacon systems. One was called the Radar Data Processing (RDP) system, which was designed to help controllers maintain separation between high-altitude, high-speed aircraft en route; the other became known as the Automated Radar Terminal System (ARTS), which was designed to accommodate the local conditions of particular airports and a mix of aircraft types.[180] As a result, the basic architecture of the NAS became segmented, with different segments to be phased in over time during the late 1960s and early 1970s.

MITRE provided a range of technical services throughout the development of the NAS and its components. The company helped prepare original specifications and established criteria to evaluate competing proposals for hardware and software. It also maintained and analyzed air traffic activity forecasts to enable appropriate deployment of computing and storage capacity and to anticipate future systems requirements. In 1965, the company established a site at Atlantic City Airport to support testing and evaluation at the FAA's National Aviation Facilities Experimental Center, later to become the William J. Hughes Technical Center.[181]

David Israel (l.) and Howard Kirschner directed the SATIN program and other MITRE projects for the FAA during the 1960s.

180. Nolan, *Fundamentals of Air Traffic Control*, 346–347.

The first segment of the NAS to be specified was the ARTS. In 1964, MITRE developed the prototype system, which was installed in Atlanta. This system tested successfully, as did a second installation in New York City two years later. Lessons learned from these experiences were incorporated into the design and development of an enhanced system, ARTS-III, which was rolled out in airports across the country during the early 1970s.[182]

Meanwhile, MITRE performed similar services in the development of the en route control system. The first phase was development of a Flight Data Processing (FDP) system to automate filing, storage, and electronic distribution and updating of flight plans. The second phase involved development of the RDP system for en route control. The combination of these two systems—FDP and RDP—became known as the NAS Stage A. Again, MITRE's assistance included system specification, technical evaluation of acquisition proposals, and testing throughout the development process. During the late 1960s, the FAA opened several prototype ARTCCs along the East Coast and then added more in the central and western states. In March 1970, the first NAS Stage A computer and software was installed in the Los Angeles ARTCC. By 1975, 20 centers had become fully operational across the continental United States, with smaller facilities in Anchorage, Honolulu, and San Juan, Puerto Rico. These installations featured automated route conversion, time calculation, association checking, and hand-off initiation.

The implementation of ARTS-III and NAS Stage A ended the era of shrimp boats and other manual aids and marked a fundamental advance in air traffic control and a major achievement in systems engineering and integration. Henceforth, controllers relied on computer-based systems to identify, track, and update the progress of aircraft throughout all stages of flight. MITRE played an essential role in the development of the National Airspace System, and its increasing responsibilities were reflected in significant growth of technical staff supporting the FAA. By 1972, about 150 personnel were engaged in FAA projects in Washington and Atlantic City.

Enhancing the NAS

The very success of the National Airspace System created new challenges, especially in introducing improvements, enhancements, and new capabilities. These challenges were both technical and organizational: technical, because it would never be a simple matter to integrate new features into a complex system that was operating continuously and could not tolerate down time; and

181. "Air Traffic Control: Looking Toward the Next Generation," 16–19.

182. Nolan, *Fundamentals of Air Traffic Control*, 347-348; "Air Traffic Control: Looking Toward the Next Generation," 28; MITRE Corporation, *MITRE: The First Twenty Years*, 77 and 141–142.

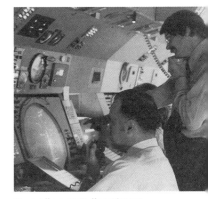

Controllers at Dulles Airport in 1972 use the newly-installed ARTS-III system to control air traffic in the terminal vicinity.

organizational, because the system's reliability made the people who operated, maintained, and used it view the prospect of making changes with understandable caution.

Even before the NAS became fully operational, however, there were concerns about its future. In 1969, the Air Traffic Control Advisory Committee of the Department of Transportation (also known as the Alexander Committee after its chair, Benjamin Alexander, chairman of General Research Corporation), an entity that included MITRE president Bob Everett, head of Washington Operations Charles Zraket, and trustees Courtland Perkins and Jack Ruina, predicted that increasing demands on the system would soon overwhelm it without near-term remedial actions. The committee identified three major problems: a shortage of terminal capacity; the need for new, more reliable ways to ensure aircraft separation; and the increasing cost of air traffic control.[183]

To address these problems, the Alexander Committee considered alternative approaches, ranging from enhancements of current technology to developing an entirely new system. In the end, cost considerations and the pressing need for near-term improvements led the Committee to recommend an incremental approach. Proposed improvements included improved systems to perform specific functions— a discrete address beacon system (DABS) to be carried aboard aircraft; a new microwave landing system to replace the very-high-frequency instrument landing system in use since the late 1940s; an upgraded VHF omni-directional-range (VOR) navigation system—and new features in the form of new decision-support tools to help controllers deal with the rising volume of air traffic.

In 1970, the FAA asked MITRE for assistance in implementing the Alexander Committee's recommendations. Under Howard Kirshner, David Bailey, and Paul Locher III, the company's Air Transportation Systems Division in Washington focused initially on developing decision-support tools to assist controllers. The first of these involved conflict detection and avoidance. SATIN and NAS Stage A had provided for "protected airspace" (minimum separation standards) around aircraft. A MITRE team led by Laurence Culhane and Stephen Hauser developed a capability called Conflict Alert as part of the en route control system. As radar and beacons continuously updated the position and altitude of flights within a controlled airspace, a computer used this track information and predicted when separation standards between an aircraft pair might be violated. Conflict Alert caused data tags for the converging aircraft to blink on the display screens, thus alerting the controllers to take preventative action. Field installation began in the fall of 1974, and by 1976 the capability was in place in all ARTCCs.[184]

183. "Air Traffic Control: Looking Toward the Next Generation," 34-35.

Conflict Alert could provide about three minutes' advance warning of a potential violation of separation standards—enough time to help avert loss of separation but not enough to help the controller select appropriate actions in response. This need became the basis of another MITRE project, Intermittent Positive Control (IPC), a collision-avoidance system that encompassed uncontrolled aircraft as well as those managed by en route controllers. Under IPC, ground computers automatically calculated avoidance maneuvers that the controlled aircraft should take and transmitted commands to the pilot via a data link.[185] Although it was never implemented, IPC became the basis of a later, much bigger, and extremely successful program called the Traffic Alert and Collision Avoidance System (TCAS).

During the 1970s, MITRE addressed other problems highlighted by the Alexander Committee. It developed a computer program to quantify the cost reduction of automating the FAA's flight service station system and demonstrated the technique around the country. The company also studied the problem of turbulence from the wake of aircraft landing and taking off, and proposed techniques for using closely spaced parallel runways to avoid airport expansion. During this period, MITRE also began working on specifications for the new microwave landing system. Designed to be more accurate and reliable than its predecessor, the new system would also make it possible for aircraft to make curved or multi-segmented approaches to runways, an innovation that could reduce noise, help aircraft avoid populated areas, and save time and fuel.

MITRE carried its work in air traffic control abroad starting in 1973, with a program to automate air traffic control in the United Kingdom. Similar assignments in Sweden, West Germany, Venezuela, Singapore, and the Republic of China (Taiwan) soon followed. Among these, the work in West Germany proved most substantial, and for many years that nation remained the company's biggest foreign client. MITRE provided support on two projects to automate and modernize Germany's air traffic control system: a flight plan processing system and a radar data processing and display system.

From NAS to NAS Plan

The NAS greatly increased the number of aircraft each controller could handle safely and improved the FAA's overall safety record. By the end of the 1970s, however, systems designed 15 years earlier were stretched to accommodate the demands on them. The Airline Deregulation Act of 1978 escalated competitive rivalry in the airline industry by allowing new entrants, expanding routes, and lowering prices. Commuter airlines grew at especially fast rates. In the early

184. MITRE Corporation, *MITRE: The First Twenty Years*, 144.

185. Ibid, 144.

Barry Horowitz, Kant Patel, and David Bailey look on as Charles Zraket solos in the general aviation trainer simulator at MITRE's Washington Operations in 1973.

1980s, moreover, some airlines and freight companies began organizing their operations in hub-and-spoke networks. The economic advantages of these arrangements were powerful, but they depended on tight scheduling and coordination of flights, resulting in yet more strains on the NAS.[186]

In these circumstances, some top FAA officials and congressional leaders believed that the only solution was a major effort to modernize the infrastructure supporting the NAS. In building the case for change, critics of the NAS pointed to the advancing age of the equipment in the ARTCCs and terminal control facilities. They noted that it was difficult to expand the capacity or capability of these systems, while costs of maintenance and replacement parts continued to soar. The NAS also had limitations that more modern technology could overcome. Separation assurance monitoring, for example, still required controllers to coordinate conflict-free clearances and track aircraft movements visually. Reported system errors—losses of the required minimum separation between aircraft—were most often attributed to controller inattention, poor judgment, and inadequate coordination and communications. New technology might rectify these problems.

186. Richard H. K. Vietor, *Contrived Competition: Regulation and Deregulation in America* (New York: Cambridge University Press, 1994), 4; Christopher D. Wickens, Anne S. Mavor, and James P. McGee, eds., *Flight to the Future: Human Factors in Air Traffic Control* (Washington, D.C.: National Academy Press, 1997), 27–28.

Another set of problems embedded in the NAS stemmed from rigid procedures to keep controller workloads manageable. Procedural restrictions, for example, limited traffic on the most desirable routes and controlled altitude profiles and schedules. Although such restrictions were meant to assure safety, they were often unnecessary in areas of relatively low traffic. The system grew still more rigid following an unsuccessful strike by the air traffic controllers in 1981, which resulted in a 50 percent reduction in controller staff. In response to these difficulties and to maintain safety, the FAA instituted Traffic Flow Management (TFM), a set of techniques and procedures that empowered controllers to manage traffic by holding aircraft on the ground until the en route system could accommodate them. TFM remained in place for an indefinite period while the FAA considered the long-term questions of how, and how much, to modernize the NAS.

The advocates of major change soon had their day. In January 1982, FAA Administrator J. Lynn Helms issued the National Air Space Plan (NAS Plan), a $9 billion, bold and comprehensive program to renovate the NAS infrastructure over a twenty-year period. The new systems were to be developed by 1992, with full implementation achieved by 2000. The first phase would involve replacing the 1960s-era computers at the heart of the NAS Stage A and ARTS systems. The second phase, scheduled to begin in the mid-1980s, would introduce a new Advanced Automation System (AAS) featuring new controller workstations and software. Finally, the greater efficiency and capability of these new systems would permit consolidation of 20 en route and 80 terminal installations into 23 combined facilities.[187]

The FAA planned to implement AAS, which would feature new hardware and software designed with the flexibility to accommodate new and higher-level automation functions, in stages. The first, in the mid-1980s, would improve the computing capacity and reliability of the en-route system infrastructure through the introduction of a new host computer while retaining the software of the existing system. The second phase entailed a new system design for the late 1980s that would include new hardware and software and redesigned facilities, including upgrades in terminal automation based on technology developed for the en route system.

187. MITRE Corporation, Operations Highlights, May 1983, 27-28.

To provide primary technical assistance to this ambitious undertaking, the FAA awarded a 10-year contract worth more than $1 billion to Martin Marietta, and it appeared that MITRE's work for the FAA would shrink dramatically. Between 1980 and 1982, the number of MITRE technical staff supporting the FAA plunged from 230 to just over 100 and there was talk of winding down the company's work on civilian air traffic control altogether. Several veteran executives in MITRE's Air Transportation Systems Division left the company and leadership of the division passed into the hands of John Fearnsides, a former deputy secretary and chief scientist in the Department of Transportation.

Jack Fearnsides joined MITRE in1982 after a distinguished career at the FAA.

Fearnsides and his management team carved out a new role for MITRE to support the modernization effort. With Martin Marietta responsible for classical systems engineering and integration responsibilities, MITRE concentrated on R&D work and operations requirements development, using powerful new computer workstations to validate requirements. This work marked the start of a 15-year effort to introduce evolutionary system development techniques to begin replacing large-scale, "big-bang" acquisitions. The effort yielded improvements in surveillance and identification systems and the evolution of new applications that could be added to the AAS. The surveillance system was based on Mode S beacon technology developed by the FAA and Lincoln Laboratory, with technical assistance from MITRE. This system provided a reliable air-ground digital data link and supported the air-to-air communication component of a new collision-avoidance capability called TCAS.

TCAS had originated with a MITRE proposal in 1975. The system was an onboard tool that identified traffic within 5 to 40 miles of the aircraft, warned pilots of impending loss of separation, and recommended actions to avoid such losses. In its initial incarnation, TCAS was a low-cost system providing only traffic advisories indicating the relative positions of intruding aircraft. TCAS II, which followed in the 1980s, provided additional features, including "resolution advisories," to enable escape maneuvers by climbing or diving. MITRE developed and tested TCAS I and TCAS II, derived and specified algorithms for surveillance and collision avoidance, performed the operational evaluation of systems onboard airline aircraft, and developed domestic and international standards.[188] The system proved highly successful in enhancing safety and became required equipment on all passenger aircraft with 30 or more seats.

Another key innovation of the 1980s was a MITRE-inspired capability called the Automated En Route Air Traffic Control (AERA) System. This capability had originated in a 1973 independent R&D study in which MITRE engineers had imagined key elements of a future air traffic control system, including the use of automated decision-support tools, to assist controllers in their work. These "human-centered" tools would remain vigilant for potential problems and, once detected, offer notification and aids for their solution. AERA was conceived as the laboratory prototype of one such decision-support tool. Using algorithms that MITRE developed, AERA would automatically support controllers' routine functions—aircraft separation, traffic flow, and clearance generation, delivery, and acknowledgment. Benefits of the system included higher controller productivity, fewer errors, and greater freedom of flight movements to save time and fuel.[189]

During the early 1980s, MITRE developed a small-scale model of the AERA system in a testbed in McLean, Virginia. The success of this demonstration led the FAA in 1983 to incorporate AERA into the AAS program. The implementation plan was divided into three stages: AERA 1, designed to allow increased user-preferred (primarily fuel-efficient) routes by 1992; AERA 2, intended to include the capability by the mid-1990s to present alternative possible solutions to conflict problems identified in AERA 1; and AERA 3, a still more advanced system to be implemented after 1997. In its ultimate form, AERA would nearly automate the aircraft separation function, enabling controllers to plan strategies to increase overall air traffic control efficiency and accommodate the preferences of airspace users.

AERA's development proved more difficult and protracted than originally planned because the system affected core controller operations and required changes to some FAA-mandated procedures. To address these problems, in the mid-1980s, MITRE engineers began collaborative development with teams of controllers, seeking their input on AERA's design and features. The result was significant progress, and a key lesson learned. From that point forward, the company worked interactively with controller teams and other FAA officials to facilitate the integration of AERA and other systems into the complex systems architecture that the FAA had already established.

188. U.S. Office of Technology Assessment, *Safer Skies with TCAS: Traffic Alert and Collision Avoidance System: Special Report* (Washington, D.C., 1989); MITRE, Transportation Systems Work Program, September 1990, 137; Transportation Systems Work Program, July 1994, 116.

189. Lawrence Goldmuntz, John T. Kefaliotis, Louis A. Kleiman, Richard A. Rucker, Leonard Schuchman, and D. Weathers, *The AERA Concept* (Federal Aviation Administration, March 1981), Preface.

Facing page:

The Airline Deregulation Act of 1978 and the coming of hub-and-spoke networks magnified crowding at airports and in the skies.

190. Tekla S. Perry, "In Search of the Future of Air Traffic Control," *IEEE Spectrum* (August 1997), 23-24; Fearnsides interview, September 3, 1997.

191. John Fearnsides interview, September 3, 1997.

192. "Sponsoring Agreement between the Federal Aviation Administration and the MITRE Corporation for Operation of the Center for Advanced Aviation System Development a Federally Funded Research and Development Center," 1.

Although TCAS and AERA consumed much of its attention during the 1980s, MITRE also worked on other improvements to the NAS. One study investigated the causes of human error, capitalizing on MITRE's experience in human factors. Other MITRE projects included a controller education program in human capabilities and limitations; a system that enabled pilots to access an automated weather database; and a basic algorithm to help the FAA estimate the impact of existing and proposed procedures on fuel consumption—a technique also used by the Air Force.

Changing Roles

In the late 1980s and early 1990s, technical problems in implementing the NAS Plan and burgeoning cost overruns led the FAA to rethink the direction of the program. The FAA eventually abandoned key features of the NAS Plan, including the AAS, the microwave landing system, and the plan to consolidate the ARTCCs and terminal radar approach control facilities. These moves were embedded in a shift in systems acquisition strategy. Rather than undertake a sweeping modernization program, the FAA announced instead the Capital Improvement Program, an evolutionary approach to upgrading its infrastructure that was similar to the asset renewal policies of commercial organizations. When Martin Marietta's systems engineering and integration contract expired, the FAA redefined management responsibilities, designating a bigger role for MITRE to do complex analyses of the interactions among individual NAS programs and systems, while engaging TRW Inc. as contractor for systems engineering and technical assistance.[190]

The FAA's shift in thinking about NAS modernization carried profound consequences for MITRE. The first step, in 1989, was a new five-year agreement with the FAA that nearly doubled the technical support MITRE had provided during its previous contract.[191] The second step was the FAA's decision in 1990 to acknowledge the company's de facto role as a Federally Funded Research and Development Center with de jure sponsorship.[192] MITRE formed the Center for Advanced Aviation System Development (CAASD) as its second FFRDC and named Fearnsides as director. As systems architect for the FAA, CAASD's responsibilities included analysis of air traffic control system requirements, design, specifications to field test, and integration of complete systems.

An early sign of CAASD's expanded responsibility was the opening of its Integration and Interaction Laboratory (I-Lab) in 1990. The I-Lab housed impressive simulation capabilities that enabled engineers and researchers to study how systems worked together and how innovations introduced in one area might affect other systems and the operation of the air traffic management system as a

In the 1970s and 1980s, the MITRE-developed Automated En Route Air (AERA) system represented an early decision-support tool to help controllers manage a growing workload.

whole. The I-Lab provided a working environment in which MITRE engineers, FAA personnel, and flight crews could test and analyze new air traffic management techniques. In the mid-1990s, for example, one team conducted experiments to develop concept descriptions for the future air traffic control system, while another explored new concepts for oceanic flight procedures.[193]

In its expanded role, MITRE supported the FAA, other international civil aviation authorities, and the aviation industry in other ways. One of the most significant involved the integration of the Global Positioning System (GPS), a satellite-based, radio navigation, position, and time transfer system originally developed for the military, into the NAS. MITRE's involvement with GPS dated to the late 1970s, when it worked on the technology with several DOD customers. GPS had obvious applications in civil aviation, especially as part of global navigation and communications systems. Using satellites to support these functions had significant economic benefits. It became possible, for example, to track aircraft over the oceans or remote land masses without investing in ground-based radar and communications networks. Commercial carriers could reach their destinations through new and direct routes, with savings of millions of dollars annually in fuel costs alone. Finally, GPS was cheaper and more accurate than alternative technologies—the microwave landing system, for instance—for controlling landings.

Although MITRE recommended the use of GPS in civilian aviation, the military, for understandable reasons, was initially reluctant to make the technology widely available. This technology, after all, represented a significant advantage for U.S. forces against an enemy without it. Meanwhile, commercial enterprises developed versions of the GPS that were only slightly less accurate than the military's and did not include the secure, anti-jamming features. These commercial systems became available for use in civilian aircraft and marine vessels, and pressure mounted for the FAA and international aviation authorities to work together to develop GPS technology and standards. By the early 1990s, the technology could no longer be contained. Amid protests from some military authorities, FAA Administrator James B. Busey IV (a retired admiral and future MITRE trustee), negotiated agreements with suppliers, airlines, and international aviation authorities to use GPS technology throughout civilian and commercial aviation.[194]

CAASD performed advanced development work on the GPS system and designed tests to demonstrate the capability to provide precision approaches to near the critical decision height of 200 feet. Intrigued by such demonstrations, the FAA investigated the possibility of adapting GPS as the primary navigation system

Opened in 1990, the Integration and Interaction Laboratory at CAASD enables researchers to identify and evaluate interoperability issues created by combining discrete systems.

193. MITRE Corporation, Annual Reports for 1993 and 1994.

194. Admiral James Busey interview, November 4, 1997.

within U.S. airspace, with CAASD again providing technical support. By early in the next century, it is expected that more advanced GPS receivers will enable controllers and flight crews to manage precision approaches into very crowded airports such as Narita, Heathrow, Kennedy, and O'Hare regardless of weather conditions. This is an important step—along with cockpit-based situation displays—in maintaining airport capacity at clear-weather levels at all times.

In the early 1990s, CAASD also served as project engineer for the Aeronautical Telecommunications Network (ATN), a global digital data communications architecture. Working with various stakeholder groups—airlines, avionics manufacturers, aeronautical communications service providers, and the FAA— MITRE helped develop the components needed to assemble an early version of the ATN, test those components, and evaluate them during extended in-service flights. MITRE also developed prototype ATN component systems.[195] To facilitate this research and development and to find an implementation path, CAASD led the creation of a public-private partnership among the stakeholders. This step highlighted CAASD's ability to work across organizational boundaries and illustrated the growing willingness of government and industry groups to facilitate innovation through new institutional forms.

In 1992, the number of technical staff at CAASD approached 450. As CAASD grew and became more visible, it became subject to the same congressional scrutiny and industry criticisms that simultaneously affected other FFRDCs, including MITRE's DOD FFRDC. (*See Interlude 5.*) These pressures led Congress and the FAA in 1993 to redefine the agency's relationship to CAASD. A new ceiling capped funding for CAASD at 335 staff years, resulting in an employment cutback of about 25 percent. At the same time, CAASD's funding became a line item in the FAA budget, where it would continue under scrutiny. The changes did not affect the substance of CAASD's roles and responsibilities, however. In 1995, the partnership between the FAA and MITRE was renewed for another five-year term and the ceiling inched up again in 1998.[196]

The Paradigm Shift

In the mid-1990s, it was increasingly clear both to the FAA and to users of the NAS that "bold innovations" to the system would be necessary to meet growing demand. The NAS still relied on both TFM techniques and classical separation assurance procedures, a combination that kept controller workloads manageable and ensured safety, but at increasing frustration and economic cost to users of the airspace. The system was rife with rigid procedures and structures developed in a different time

Retired U.S. Navy Admiral James B. Busey IV served as FAA administrator and negotiated implementation of the Global Positioning System. Later Busey became a MITRE trustee.

195. MITRE Corporation, Annual Report for 1993.

196. Fearnsides interview, September 3, 1997.

and context. Inefficiencies in the NAS, estimated one expert in 1997, "are costing the airlines over $3 billion annually." The system, moreover, was

enormously complex. 5,000 aircraft are airborne at any given time. Thousands of decision makers are actively ensuring that the system is safe and efficient. The complex nature of air traffic involves thousands of decisions by each category of user to maintain the integrity of a schedule and thus the economic integrity of the operation. It is virtually impossible for the FAA to run an efficient operation without frequent collaboration with its users at all levels from preflight and schedule planning to tactical aircraft maneuvers.[197]

In these circumstances, the FAA and users of the NAS began to look for new ways to "manage"—as opposed to "control"—air traffic. In a process in which MITRE played, and continues to play, a key role, the stakeholders in the modernization of NAS began to outline a new approach to Collaborative Air Traffic Management, "in which safety decisions are made by the FAA and economic decisions are made by the user." To those affected, the move from Air Traffic Control to Air Traffic Management represented "a monumental paradigm shift...from separation assurance to separation assurance plus traffic flow management."[198]

The shape of Collaborative ATM began to emerge in an FAA/industry/CAASD initiative in the early 1990s called the Traffic Flow Management Architecture and Requirements Team (TFM-ART). This marked the first time that leaders across the FAA's main business and operational units sat down for an extended period with industry leaders to define a vision of the future air traffic system. The group's work was refined in a broader ATM context in the RTCA Task Force 3 on Free Flight meetings in the mid-1990s, and information exchange explicitly was detailed in RTCA Special Committee 169 Working Group 5 on Ground-to-Ground communications.[199]

Such collaboration began to move the FAA towards greater emphasis on service and performance, critical elements of the agency's growth into the 21st century. At the same time, the new approach improved the efficiency of the NAS for all parties by giving each a stake in the identification and resolution of flow inefficiencies. Critical components of Collaborative ATM were broad-based information exchange leading to common situation awareness and sharing of advanced decision-support capabilities to support planning and strategy assessment.

In support of the Collaborative ATM approach, CAASD conducted extensive research to develop a decision-support system that would make possible more flexible routings while ensuring system safety. A research study found, for example, that airport capacity was not the only constraint on the growth of

197. Statement of Margaret T. Jenny, Director, Operations Research, US Airways, before the House Committee on Science, Subcommittee on Technology, June 24, 1997, 26–27. In addition to her responsibilities at US Airways, Jenny served as a member of the FAA's Research Engineering and Development Advisory Committee, and Co-chairperson of the RTCA Free Flight Select Committee.

198. Ibid, 27.

199. RTCA Inc. is a private not-for-profit organization that serves as a Utilized Federal Advisory Committee.

air traffic. Another was the rigid structures—the "highways in the sky"—of the en route control system. New technologies, especially a set of decision-support tools to assist controllers, offered a partial solution to both problems. These new tools would draw on inputs from the managers of the airspace and its users in making more flexible decisions in areas that affect user economics such as routes and schedules. Under certain conditions, aircraft could fly more direct routes to their destinations.

CAASD worked with FAA officials, controllers, and representatives of airspace users to develop the new decision-support tools. Initial research focused on TFM decision making around issues such as, ground delay programs, sequencing, or severe weather avoidance that could affect whole populations of aircraft and alter the timing and efficiency of hub-and-spoke operations. The goal was to develop new ways to make TFM decisions collaboratively, with users first proposing actions to help resolve problems.

To accommodate this need and also ensure safety, controllers required greater advance warning of potential conflicts between aircraft. Applying its knowledge base developed during AERA, CAASD engineers worked closely with FAA officials and controllers to design the User Request Evaluation Tool (URET), a sophisticated decision-support system to help manage potential conflicts in the sky. The system obtains real-time flight plan and track data from air traffic control computers and combines these with weather information and other data to build four-dimensional aircraft flight profiles, or trajectories, for its own use and for display to controllers. URET also adapts itself to the observed behavior of aircraft, dynamically adjusting predicted speeds, climb rates, and descent rates based on the performance of each flight as it is tracked en route. URET then uses the predicted trajectories to detect potential aircraft problems up to 20 minutes into the future—in contrast to the three minutes' warning of Conflict Alert—and to provide a strategic alert to the appropriate sector. Trajectories are also the basis for trial planning, which allows a controller to check a desired flight plan amendment for potential conflicts before a clearance is issued—an improved capability for handling pilot requests.[200]

In short, URET allows aircraft to fly more direct routes, which yields significant savings in fuel and other expenses. URET shifts the controller's perspective from tactical to strategic concerns and facilitates more effective planning. In the late 1990s, URET was being tested in several FAA operations centers, with the goal of making the tool widely available to controllers by early in the 21st century.

Facing page:

Using flight plans, in-flight data, weather reports, and other sources, the User Request Evaluation Tool (URET) allows controllers to "see" up to 20 minutes into the future and detect potential conflicts well before they become serious.

200. MITRE Corporation, URET: User Request Evaluation Tool, unpublished, undated document.

Modernization, Part II

In the late 1990s, CAASD was addressing challenges and opportunities that extend well into the 21st century. In addition to its continuing work on GPS and Collaborative ATM, the company is exploring new institutional arrangements to support its mission. In 1997, MITRE once again showed itself an institutional innovator, establishing a new, nonprofit affiliate, which partnered with ARINC, a communications company owned by United States and international airlines and aircraft operators, to form a new company called SkySource. Using advanced Internet-based technologies, SkySource provides a single, integrated source of aeronautical information to airspace users and the FAA.[201]

201. MITRE Corporation, Annual Report for 1997.

MITRE also broadened its international scope through CAASD, by 1998 providing technical assistance to nearly 40 countries outside the United States. With the globalization of the economy came an increasing need for international collaboration and more integrated systems. CAASD provided systems engineering and research and development support to civil aviation authorities worldwide in airport operations, system design and development, safety, and global communications, navigation, and surveillance. CAASD also worked with various countries and international organizations to support airport privatization initiatives and to evaluate options for increasing capacity and reducing delays.

In late 1997, CAASD took on a new role for the FAA and users of the national airspace as facilitator of the NAS Modernization Task Force. Established by FAA Administrator Jane Garvey, the task force was formed to bring together high-level decision makers from the government and private sector: top FAA officials, officers of the controllers' and maintenance employees' unions, operating executives of the airlines, and airframe manufacturers engaged in developing and maintaining the overall system. Garvey was particularly concerned to identify the barriers to modernization and to recommend ways to overcome them. Fearnsides served as facilitator to the Task Force, with CAASD personnel providing staff assistance and analysis. A tool that helped the Task Force move ahead quickly was a "risk reduction matrix" that arrayed major elements of a proposed new system architecture against institutional procedures and interests among the government and user communities. This matrix helped to identify areas of greater or lesser concern in implementing the new architecture. It also helped focus discussion and negotiation among members of the Task Force, identify and rank priorities, and develop a revised implementation plan with discrete phases, once again building on the 15-year concentration on evolutionary development approaches.[202]

While it attended to current assignments in the late 1990s, CAASD also kept an eye on the future challenges of air traffic management. Several points seemed certain. First, demand for air commerce will continue to soar in the 21st century. Second, the increasingly interdependent nature of the global economy will increase the need for new international standards and systems compatibility. Third, the rapid pace of innovation in information technology is unlikely to taper off. And finally, all of these developments will have a significant impact on air traffic management.

CAASD's leaders also recognized many unanswered questions about the future of the company's work: What will be the specific effects of new technology on air traffic management? How can safety be enhanced and costs reduced? How can automation support decision makers most effectively? Who will pay for improvements? How will roles and responsibilities evolve? What will CAASD's role be?

As they considered these questions, CAASD's leaders drew lessons from the past. The most powerful forces for change in air traffic management were users of the system: airlines, aircraft operators, and ultimately the flying public. These constituencies demanded—and proved willing to pay for—safety, value, and flexibility. In the ongoing quest to improve performance along these dimensions, the skills and capabilities CAASD acquired during its first four decades—its long experience in air traffic control, its deep knowledge of technology and systems, and its impressive understanding of institutional environments—augur well.

202. James Kingsbury and Catherine Howland interview, May 26, 1998; NAS Modernization Task Force, Revised Approach to NAS Modernization (presentation text and graphics, n.d.)

1   Developed in the mid-1990s, the MITRE Information Infrastructure (MII) represents one of the most versatile intranets in existence.

2   Foreshadowing a new era in office automation, the Collaborative Virtual Workspace enables scattered personnel to work together in real time.

3   In 1996 top management commissioned the cross-functional Innovation Team (I-Team) to help ensure MITRE's continuing leadership in information technology.

March 18
Force XXI experiment is successfully completed at U.S. Army National Training Center

April
Electronic Systems Center designates MITRE as information systems architect

January
MITRE begins work for FBI in critical infrastructure protection

March 11
U.S. Government delivers first AWACS to Japan

April
Air Traffic Control modernization work in China begins

July 21
MITRE marks 40th anniversary of incorporation

July
U.S. Internal Revenue Service selects MITRE to operate FFRDC to support modernization of IRS information systems

June
Intelink TS has 40,000 users and is accessed more than 300,000 times per week

June
Peace Shield (Saudi Arabia Air Defense System) is completed ahead of schedule; it is the largest foreign military sales program undertaken by DOD

August 12
Ft. Franklin V (FFV) demonstrates ESC battlespace integration and test laboratory

September 12
17 Nations sign Regional Air Space Management Initiative for Eastern Europe. United States offers MITRE technical assistance under ESC/IA leadership

October 2
Defense Under Secretary Dr. Paul G. Kaminski cites MITRE and other FFRDC's as "critical national assets"

August
FAA decides to deploy "en route conflict probe" based on MITRE CAASD User Request Evaluation Tool (URET)

September 18
U.S. Air Force celebrates its 50th Anniversary

September 19
Air Force presents Pioneer Award to MITRE

September 30
SkySource, a joint venture to provide integrated aeronautical information, is formed

Epilogue
MITRE at Forty

MITRE at Forty

Late in 1997, on the eve of MITRE's 40th year, two top-level government reviews underscored the high and growing significance of information technology to the economic health and national security of the United States. The President's Commission on Critical Infrastructure Protection focused on how information technology has established "a complex network of interdependence" that connects and interpenetrates such essential civilian services as energy, banking and finance, transportation, vital human services, and telecommunications. To the Commission, this network constitutes "a new dimension of vulnerability, which, when combined with an emerging constellation of threats, poses unprecedented national risk." Meanwhile, the National Defense Panel proclaimed that "the importance of maintaining America's lead in information systems—commercial and military— cannot be overstated. Our nation's economy will depend on a secure and assured information infrastructure."[203]

Chairman James Schlesinger (l.) and President Victor DeMarines project a continuing vital role for MITRE as new technologies transform and reshape critical government operations.

203. Both reports quoted in MITRE Corporation, Annual Report for 1997.

Such conclusions signal not only the far-reaching impact of information technology on America's position and influence in global affairs, but also the vital role of institutions like MITRE in helping to preserve America's lead. Reflecting on MITRE's first four decades—and also looking ahead—Trustee Chairman James Schlesinger and President Vic DeMarines see ample reason to be proud of the company's achievements and optimistic about its future. These leaders point out that the company is well positioned to lead, support, and benefit from the continuing transformation of critical government functions. Schlesinger traces the roots of this transformation back to SAGE, which used computers to revolutionize the air defense function, although back then no one understood or foresaw the pervasive impact of computers and information technology on government operations. Both leaders now proclaim the same message: as DeMarines puts it,

The past ten years have demonstrated the incredible impact of information technology throughout society and the economy. Look at the phenomenal growth of the Internet, the explosion in software and hardware development. Now consider the impact—how borders and barriers are breaking down. There's more teamwork, collaboration, and cooperation across organizational boundaries and geographical borders. We live in a world that runs on information. Information technology is reshaping everything—industry, financial services, higher education, and now the government. And it's just the beginning of what is to come.

MITRE is perfectly placed to help the government take advantage of this technology. We still need defense, albeit of a different order than during the Cold War. Information technology is making America's defense more efficient and lethal even if the scale of our forces is smaller. In defense and air traffic management, there will be a continuing need for technical support and understanding of the evolutionary path of systems development. This also plays to MITRE's strengths. The company has become a critical national resource.[204]

Evidence to support this view lies in many recent programs and initiatives. Intelink revolutionized the gathering and dissemination of intelligence information and changed the way the intelligence community operates. The battlefield systems exhibited in the Army's Force XXI Advanced Warfare Experiments are transforming the nature of combat. The Global Positioning System, decision-support systems such as the MITRE-developed User Request Evaluation Tool, and new information resources such as SkySource are facilitating significant improvements in the management of air traffic, with notable benefits in safety, efficiency, and convenience.

204. James Schlesinger interview, November 4, 1997; Victor DeMarines interview, December 3, 1997; MITRE Corporation, Annual Report for 1997.

The transforming potential of information technology on government operations is also evident in MITRE's engagements with its newest sponsors. In 1998, the U.S. Internal Revenue Service chose MITRE to operate a new FFRDC to assist the government in its ongoing effort to modernize systems for tax administration. The selection represented a significant new responsibility to help with a pressing government need. The specific nature of MITRE's assignment will involve strategic assistance and advice in the process of modernization, and it will draw on the company's expertise in engineering both information technology and operational processes. The FFRDC leadership team includes Senior Vice President Gene Cross as the FFRDC's executive director and Bill Hutzler as FFRDC director, along with Mike Blom (who led the submission team) and Diane Schulte as program directors.

In 1997, the Air Force engaged MITRE as systems architect in developing its new, integrated command and control system. The choice of terminology—systems architect, as opposed to systems engineer—was deliberate and emphasized an expanded role that subsumed MITRE's traditional systems engineering and integration support to the Service. As systems architect, MITRE became responsible not only for technical assistance in design, development, procurement, and evaluation of discrete systems, but also for coordinating the interrelationships between and among these systems. As architect, MITRE will work with the Air Force to develop a new information infrastructure to enable discrete systems to work together. It will also support the Air Force as the infrastructure and the systems connected with it evolve over time through spiral development of upgrades and new generations of technology.

205. Air & Space Command and Control, Four-Star Read Ahead (Presentation text and graphics), April 7, 1997.

206. Harold Sorenson interviews, October 1, 1997 and January 23, 1998; Harold W. Sorenson, The Command and Control Platform (MITRE Presentation text and graphics), May 1996.

MITRE's new role emerged in the aftermath of the major U.S. military operations of the 1990s—the Gulf conflict and Bosnia—which revealed the power of information technology in combat and peacekeeping missions but also exposed some frustrating limitations in the interoperability of various electronic systems. JTIDS, AWACS, Joint STARS, and many other Air Force systems in command and control, communications, intelligence, surveillance, and reconnaissance were each developed in isolation, or as "stovepipes." Systems developed by one branch of the military tended to use different standards and protocols from those developed elsewhere. Strategic systems differed from tactical systems. Systems developed by one nation in an allied operation tended to be incompatible with systems developed by coalition partners.

Systems of different provenance can sometimes be patched together through clever interfaces and skillful integration techniques, but the process is costly and fraught with difficulty and the results often mixed. A better approach—illustrated by the phenomenal growth of the Internet, applications like Intelink, or the Army's Force XXI systems—is to develop a common information infrastructure or "information utility" to support all different systems. Such is the logic behind the new Air Force command and control system, which will break down the stovepipes and facilitate interoperability of systems developed by the all branches of the U.S. military, and foreign allies.[205]

In 1998, the U.S. Internal Revenue Service selected MITRE to operate a new FFRDC. Pictured at the signing of the contract: (standing l. to r.) IRS officials Myron Pankiw and John Roberts, Bill Hutzler (MITRE), Greg Rothwell (IRS), Gene Cross, Mike Blom, and David Hodulich (MITRE), Derrick Heard and Jerry Lewis (IRS), and Diane Schulte (MITRE). Seated are Michelle Faseru (IRS) and Roger Furr (MITRE).

Encouraged by MITRE, the Air Force now considers the acquisition of a command and control system in the same way that it views the acquisition of a new aircraft. According to Harold W. Sorenson, senior vice president and general manager of MITRE's Center for Air Force C^2 Systems, "Command and control rightfully should be a single system like an airplane is a single system":

When the Air Force builds an airplane, say the F-22, it creates a single program office. That office coordinates the development of the engine, the airframe and structures, the electronics, the flight control, and other components and subsystems. When the separate pieces come together, they work together. Until now, command and control systems have not been developed that way. To continue the airplane analogy, the engine is developed in one place, the electronics someplace else, and the structures in still another place. The result is a plane that doesn't fly. That's why we had interoperability problems in command and control in Desert Storm and Bosnia. And to avoid such problems is why we're working with the Air Force to develop a new systems architecture for command and control.[206]

In 1997, the Air Force Electronic Systems Center reorganized to emphasize functional C^2 components and their integration and set up the new Chief Architect's Office. At the same time, MITRE set up a parallel organization and provided staff to the new office. The Air Force also established a new central organization, the Air and Space C² Agency, at Langley Air Force Base, to lead the integration effort across all major commands, and MITRE serves as the liaison between the new organization and ESC.

The result of these changes, says Lieutenant General Ronald Kadish, commander of ESC, is a new, more interdependent relationship evolving between the Air Force and the company: "We're moving from a model in which we oversee our contractor to a technical partnership to accomplish this integration task." Kadish also credits MITRE's assistance in developing a range of management innovations, such as architecture councils and other integration activities, to address the extremely difficult technical and organizational challenges of making the new C² system come to life. The Air Force is even applying a lesson from the Army by designing Expeditionary Forces Experiments to develop and test new C² capabilities.[207]

For his part, Sorenson stresses that the Air Force's new approach to developing its C² system—and MITRE's role in supporting it—are as significant as anything in the relationship between the service and the company since the development of SAGE. In its 40th year, MITRE's history came full circle.[208]

MITRE's 40th birthday provides an opportunity to reflect on continuity, change, and challenge in the company's history. The continuities are evident: MITRE still pursues its original mission to serve the public interest and operates under the same rules and restrictions it embraced at its birth. It remains fully committed to its earliest customers, the Air Force and the FAA, as well as to its newer customers in the DOD, intelligence community, foreign governments, and the IRS. The company is still regarded as an invaluable national resource in systems engineering and integration, disciplines in which it has earned world-class distinction. MITRE continues to attract and retain talented scientists, engineers, and managers who are motivated by public service and challenging work as much or more than by money and professional renown. And the company continues to carry out both sponsored and independent research to expand its capabilities, advance knowledge, and better serve its customers.

Yet changes in MITRE's circumstances are also apparent. The company serves a broad array of customers within DOD and the intelligence community, as well as the FAA and the IRS. MITRE's relationship with these customers has evolved beyond customary contractual terms to long-term partnerships in which employees and customers work side-by-side on systems development and modernization teams and share accountability for the result. The technical expertise for which MITRE is noted has moved from the specific—systems engineering and integration of radar, computer hardware and software, and communications systems for tracking aircraft

(l. to r.) Eric Skoog, Lou Metzger, Joe Derosa, Julie Surer, and Ralph Bush of MITRE's Air Force Center and ESC's Chief Architect's Office work toward full integration of Air Force command and control systems.

207. Lieutenant General Ronald Kadish interview, February 17, 1998.

208. Sorenson interview, January 23, 1998.

in real time—to the general: information architectures and systems to support a spectrum of government decision makers ranging from air traffic controllers, pilots, soldiers, naval personnel, and field commanders, up to the highest officials in the Pentagon, intelligence community, FAA, and White House. (In recognition of its growing volume of work for the federal government, in late 1998 MITRE announced plans to consolidate its Washington operations into a single complex in Tyson's Corner, Virginia, that will open in 2002.) Although most of its assignments were commissioned by the U.S. government, MITRE also supported many foreign governments in military and air traffic management programs.

During its first four decades MITRE learned a lot, acquiring deep and intimate understanding of its customers' operations and requirements and extensive experience on the frontiers of information technology. The company learned

- to collaborate and work in teams with its customers;
- to incorporate frontline feedback into real-time systems improvements;
- to share responsibility and accountability not only for the performance of the programs and projects on which it worked but for the broader missions behind them;
- to facilitate organizational change and interorganizational cooperation;
- to function in politicized environments under the scrutiny of public authorities and the press;
- to profit from fair criticism and absorb the unfair; and
- to do its job better, by capturing knowledge and experience gained in one part of the organization and transferring it throughout the company.

The most dramatic changes at MITRE reflect the new context in which it operates: a new world order taking shape in the aftermath of the Cold War and the collapse of communism; a new attitude toward government that recognizes limits to its scope of activity and stresses more efficient use of resources; and a new awareness of the centrality of information technology to virtually every significant activity of individuals and organizations in modern society.

209. Quoted in H.W. Sorenson, MITRE Center for Air Force C² Systems (CAFC2S)—Positioning for the Future (Presentation text and graphics, June 1997).

Yet for all of its optimism and accomplishment, MITRE's leaders see many challenges ahead for the company. As DeMarines put it in a 1997 speech, "We now have the opportunity to have major impact more than at any time in our history. We are also in a more fragile state than ever."[209] Chief among the concerns was the need to provide for renewal in a ceiling-constrained environment without relying on the usual strategies of growth and diversification. That lesson of recent history is evident not only to MITRE but also to its customers, who acknowledge the importance of maintaining the company's health and vitality. "It goes against fundamental human nature and our business culture in this country to ask a company to act in the public interest and not grow," admits General Kadish. "The measures of success for an FFRDC are tough. They are not traditional. They're mostly intangible. The natural measures like growth, revenues, employment, and the like can be detrimental to the fundamental mission of an FFRDC. We have to learn how to live with that."[210]

Another challenge, stressed repeatedly and alike by MITRE's leaders and its customers, is the need to ensure the objective nature of the company's advice. Sometimes MITRE's role is to deliver bad news, as illustrated by a recent company report advocating cuts in procurement of Joint STARS aircraft while awaiting development of a next-generation platform. Carrying out that recommendation affected staffing levels at the Air Force, MITRE, and the industrial contractors supporting the program. Yet both MITRE's leaders and the Air Force high command believe that the decision was the right one in the public interest.

A third challenge is attracting and retaining bright, hard-working people who possess both a mastery of technology and a dedication to public service. "The not-for-profit public interest aspect of the company is a substantial factor" in motivation at MITRE, writes Don Neuman on the occasion of his retirement in 1998 after nearly four decades at the company. "It removes corporate profit as a behavioral driver and replaces it with 'doing good' for the country. I see it time and again where the MITRE people are working to their limits to achieve best value for their government sponsors without compromise due to corporate pressure to make a profit. We are a company that wants to do its best doing the right things. That creates a very pleasant corporate culture."[211]

Looking ahead, the company's leaders remain upbeat about MITRE's prospects. "There is a continuing need for institutions like MITRE," concludes DeMarines.

In fact, I expect greater demand for our services. We have technical expertise, long experience, and intimate knowledge of our customers' requirements. The government cannot replicate these qualities nor compete with the commercial world for enough people with the requisite skills. The recipe for MITRE's success in the future is the same as it has been in the past: a combination of technical skills that are state of the art; deep understanding of our customers' missions; and the capability to define and deliver on a vision to guide future government systems. I see a bright future.

210. Kadish interview, February 17, 1998.

211. Donald Neuman to Dr. James Schlesinger, 14 May, 1998.

Oral History Interviews

Present and Former
MITRE Employees and Trustees

Branscomb, Lewis	11.24.97
Busey, James Adm.	11.04.97
Canty, William	10.07.97
	10.14.97
Cross, Gene	08.13.97
DeMarines, Victor	08.12.97
	12.03.97
Ellingson, Eric	09.29.97
	10.07.97
	10.14.97
Everett, Robert	10.24.97
Faga, Martin	09.05.97
Fearnsides, John	09.03.97
Granato, Richard	11.04.97
Horowitz, Barry	09.03.97
Kingsbury, James & Catherine Howland	05.26.98
Lehman, David	10.14.97
Martell, Donald & Aaron Lesser	10.02.97
McLucas, John	11.03.97
Neuman, Donald	10.21.97
Providakes, Jason	12.22.97
Quilty, John	12.02.97
Schlesinger, James	11.04.97
	06.08.98
Sharfman, Peter	01.07.98
Sorenson, Harold	10.01.97
	01.23.98
Spaney, Cindy	08.15.97
Starr, Stuart	12.02.97
Thomas, Lydia	11.04.97
Trasko, Darrell	10.21.97
Weiss, Andrea	12.02.97
Woodward, John	11.25.97
Zraket, Charles	10.22.97

Sponsors-Clients Interviews

Army
Brigadier General Steven Boutelle	12.22.97
Lieutenant General William Campbell	11.03.97
Victor Ferlise	12.22.97

Air Force
Lieutenant General Ronald Kadish	02.17.98

Navy
Vice Admiral Arthur Cebrowski	01.07.98

Index

Sprague, Robert, 59, 114

Sputnik, 23

Stanford University, 17

Star Wars, 86, 95, 111

Starbird, Alfred, 122

Starr, Stuart, 78, 139, 177

Stennis, Senator, 46

Strategic Air Command (SAC), 38, 86, 88, 111

Strategic Air Command Intelligence Data Handling System, 86

Strategic and tactical command and control systems, 26
    for air traffic control, 10–11, 149–151
        development of NAS as, 146–150
        enhancing NAS, 153–155
        modernization of NAS, 162–167
        NAS Plan as, 155–160
    AWACS, 43–44
        carriers of, 40–42, 57
        origins of, 44–46
        production of, 53–55
        requirements for, 46–53
    GPS, vii–viii, 117, 131, 161–162
    JTIDS, 68–70
        class 1 terminal of, 77–78
        class 2 terminals of, 78–83, 110
        as conceived by MITRE, 9, 68–70, 71–72, 123
        digital computing for, 72–73, 74, 100
        PLRACTA and, 75–76
    MITRE's 1958–1966 role in developing, 5, 29, 30, 32, 34–39
    MITRE's 1966–1976 role in developing, 62–67
    MITRE's 1976–1986 role in developing, 87–95

Strategic Command and Control: Redefining the Nuclear Threat (Blair), 95

Strategic Defense Initiative (Star Wars), 86, 95, 111

Stratton, Julius, 24

"Stringing the McNamara Line" (Greeley), 122

Sugawara, Sandra, 142

Sullivan Gordon, 128, 129, 130

Summer studies, 19

"Summer Study, The" (Marvin and Weyl), 19

Survival in the Air Age (Finletter), 16

System Development Corporation, 24

Systems Design Laboratory, 30, 31

Systems Engineering Process Office, 117

"Systems, Experts, and Computers" (Hughes and Hughes), 63

Tachmindji, Alexander, 114, 125

Tactical Air Control Center, 41

Tactical Air Control System (407L), 38, 62, 76–77

Tactical Air Control Systems/Tactical Air Defense Systems (TACS/TADS), 92

Tactical air systems *See* Strategic and tactical command and control systems

Task Force XXI, 130–135

TBM-3W Avenger, 44

TCAS, *See* Traffic Alert and Collision Avoidance System

TCP/IP protocols, 102

TDMA. *See* Time division multiple access

Technical Centers at MITRE (MITRE), 116

Texas Instruments, 30

Theater Rapid Response Intelligence Package (TRRIP), 145

Therrien, Hank, 46

Thomas, Lydia, 65, 67, 90, 91, 114, 116, 144, 177

TICCET computer-controlled television project, 58

Time division multiple access (TDMA), 73, 75
    class 1, 77–78
    class 2, 78–80
    MITRIX, 100–101

Timeline of MITRE
    from 1958 to 1966, 28–31
    from 1966 to 1976, 58–61
    from 1976 to 1986, 84–86
    from 1986 to 1990, 110–111
    from 1990 to 1996, 136–137
    from 1996 to 1998, 168–169

Tinker Air Force Base, 57

Torrejon Air Force Base, 60

Tracking and Data Relay Satellite System, 91

Track-while-scan systems, 29

Traffic Alert and Collision Avoidance System (TCAS), 110, 155, 157–158, 160

Traffic Flow Management (TFM), 156, 162

Traffic Flow Management Architecture and Requirements Team (TFM-ART), 163

Trains (high-speed) project, 58, 60, 61, 64

Trans World Airlines (TWA), 150

Trasko, Darrell, 78, 177

"Travels through Bosnia and Herzegovina to Aid TRRIP Users" (Galarowicz), 145

TRRIP, 145

Truman, Harry, 16, 25

TRW, 63, 122, 160

Turing, Alan, 72

Tuve, Merle, 44

"21st Century Defense Communications System," 110

Unified Commands, 101

United Airlines, 150

United Nations, 139

University of California, 17, 55
    Radiation Laboratory of, 25

University of Illinois, 19
    Mosaic browser of, 107, 136

University of Michigan, 17

University of Texas, 59

University of Virginia, 114

Urban Mass Transit Project, 59

URET, *See* User Request Evaluation Tool

"URET: User Request Evaluation Tool" (MITRE), 165

US Airways, 163

Use of MITRE in the DOD (MITRE), 142

User Request Evaluation Tool (URET), 11, 164, 165, 169

U.S. Postal Service, 91

"U.S. Risks Defense Decline" (Schlesinger), 4

U.S. Weather Service, 65

Vacherot, Maurice, 54, 60

Valley, George, 17–19, 22, 24

Valley Committee, 18, 19

Very High Speed Integrated Circuit (VHSIC), 80, 82

VHF omni-directional-range (VOR) navigation system, 154

Video disc technology, 85

Vietor, Richard H. K., 156

Vietnam War, 46, 55, 62, 73, 76
    battlefield systems for, 121–123

von Karman, Theodore, 17

Acknowledgements

Many people helped bring this book into being. We start by thanking the present and former trustees and officers of The MITRE Corporation who committed substantial blocks of time for oral history interviews and the review of numerous drafts of outlines, chapters, illustrations, and the book as a whole. These people are listed in the appendix, but we are particularly grateful to Chairman James Schlesinger and President Victor DeMarines, who maintained a strong interest in the project from beginning to end. Senior Vice President and Operations Officer Gene Cross oversaw the entire effort and helped to keep it on track..

Alan Shoemaker, Director of Public Affairs, and David Baldwin, the company's long-time archivist and now a member of its technical staff, poured tremendous energy into the project, facilitating interviews, removing roadblocks, assisting with research, reviewing early drafts, synthesizing comments from other readers, offering encouragement, and generally (and immeasurably) helping out. Working with Alan and Dave has been a true pleasure. In Alan's office, Barbara Vachon and Joan Sheldon provided valuable administrative assistance.

Lindy Kerr gave the manuscript a close copy-editing and chased down many photographs and illustrations. Catherine Howland and Jim Kingsbury provided special help with matters related to the Center for Advanced Aviation System Development.

Professor Thomas P. Hughes provided us with an advance copy of his work on SAGE, now published in *Rescuing Prometheus* (New York: Pantheon Books, 1998). Dr. Ruth P. Liebowitz, historian at the Electronics System Center at Hanscom AFB, facilitated research on JTIDS and AWACS.

At The Winthrop Group, Inc., Julia Heskel conducted research and interviews and drafted background material on the JTIDS and Collaborative Air Traffic Management cases. Margaret B.W. Graham made available her deep knowledge of science and technology history and made many helpful suggestions. Kathleen McDermott, a former colleague, helped get the project off the ground and conceive ways to balance text and illustrations. Suzanne Spellman provided excellent transcripts of the oral history interviews.

This book was designed by Judy Kohn and Mia Moran of Kohn Cruikshank, Inc. in Boston. In addition to their excellent design work, Judy and Mia contributed many helpful comments about the book's content. Kathy Massimini compiled the index.

About the Authors:

Davis Dyer is a founding director of
The Winthrop Group, Inc., a company
based in Cambridge, Massachusetts
and specializing in business and technology history. He is author or co-author
of many publications, including *TRW:
Pioneering Technology and Innovation
since 1900* (Boston: Harvard Business
School Press, 1998), and (with Alan
Brinkley), *The Reader's Companion to
the American Presidency* (Boston:
Houghton Mifflin, forthcoming in 1999).

Michael Aaron Dennis teaches at
Cornell University in the Department
of Science and Technology Studies.
A historian of 20th century science
and technology, he is the author of
a forthcoming study of two federally
funded research institutions—MIT's
Instrumentation Laboratory (now the
Charles Stark Draper Laboratory)
and Johns Hopkins University's Applied
Physics Laboratory—during World
War II and the postwar era.

Photography:

Photograph on page 159, Black Star

Photograph #3 on page 110 and
photograph on page 161, Stock Boston

Photograph #4 on page 111 and tank
photo on page 118, Arms Communication

Photograph of the Chicago Control
Tower on page 147, courtesy of Chicago
O'Hare International Airport

The AEGIS Cruiser photograph on
page 68, courtesy of the U.S. Navy

The Missile Defense Battery on page 69,
courtesy of Raytheon Company

The photograph of General Sullivan on
page 130, courtesy of the U.S. Army

Book design:

Mia Moran, Kohn Cruikshank Inc.
Boston, Massachusetts

Printing and binding:

Starr-Toof Printing Co., Inc.
Memphis, Tennessee

BINDTECH, Inc.
Nashville, Tennessee